Nick Baam

MALVERN

a novel

To my sons

From: Andy Read
To: Rob Baltusrol
Subj: re: by jove!

Please, no.

It's better than the hairy yarmulkes for bald Jews idea, isn't it?

On 1 May 2007, at 19:02, rob baltusrol wrote:

I have an idea.

To: Morton Library
From: Rob Baltusrol
Subj: Give me just a little more time ...

Charlis, I'm still watching Black Narcissus (again!). (Deborah Kerr, Jean Simmons, *and* Sabu?) I know it's a few days late. Do you think you could work your magic again and make those late fees disappear? Thanks.

When you do get it back, I strongly suggest you watch it with (director Michael) Powell's commentary. In it he goes into some detail about what color to make Deborah Kerr's habit, how white. They finally decided to go with oatmeal! (Why can't I have a conversation like that?)

-----Original Message-----
From: morton library
Sent to: Rob Baltusrol
Subject: Best of Film noir
Date: March 12 2007

Hi Rob;

Just a reminder: you still have the classic film noir DVD.

(Didn't you already see this?)

To: letters@nytimes.com
From: Rob Baltusrol
Subj: old script

Editor;

How come every time I see the words Al Qaeda in your newspaper, my mind thinks George Kaplan?

(Terrorism being the MacGuffin?)

(Lara Logan the latest blonde?)

From: Tom McNab
To: Rob Baltusrol
Subj: re: copy editor

Mr Baltusrol,

Thank you for your interest in the position of page designer/copy
editor at the Star-Banner. You offer an interesting and diverse resume, not
to mention one of the most compelling little notes of introduction that
I've seen in the last couple of years.

We are seriously considering an in-house candidate to fill that
spot, which would create a vacancy on the night copy desk, also for a page
designer/copy editor. Would that position interest you?
Looking forward to your reply.

-- tom mcnab
managing editor
Star-Banner

p.s. I'm a Long Islander myself. In fact, I'm pretty familiar with the East
Hampton Star because I started my career covering the Hamptons as a
reporter for Suffolk Life. Good paper, the Star.

On 24 April 2007, at 19:02, rob baltusrol wrote:

Dear Mr. McNab;

A good copy editor possesses two essential knowledges -- all that's
important, and all that's unimportant. The first allows him to make sure the
sentence reads right. The second allows him to spot the differences
between the liners Queen Elizabeth and Queen Mary, to identify May
Pang, Rosie Ruiz, and Edith Head; to know who's nonplussed and who
isn't. A good copy editor knows the names of Alfred Hitchcock's Three
Investigators, knows which four states are technically commonwealths;
that the Beatles' single 'She Loves You' was on Swan Records, and of
course how to spell bouillabaisse, Reykjavik, fuchsia, and Pete
Townshend and Spike Jonze.

Sincerely,

Rob Baltusrol

To: kooliekatering.com
From: Rob Baltusrol
Subj: that all jazz?

Suzanne;

Got the jazz festival check, thanks: but $23?? I thought there was a four-hour minimum. That was a rainy, shitty Sunday night, it was supposed to be a 7-hour shift, I absolutely would not have gone out for that. (Not with Aunt Jess in Cabot Cove.)

Was there a mistake? Thanks.

Rob

On 20 April 2007, at 11:52, kooliekatering.com wrote:

Robert,
Lonnie just called, wanted to make a point of saying how you saved Saturday night, how grateful Evelyn was. (Where'd you learn to make a 30 minute crème brule?) Thanks again.
Suzanne

From: karin@lotsalegs.com
To: Rob Baltusrol
Subj: no flowers?

our month anniversary. remember? (sure you do.)

On 1 April 2007, at 11:33, rob baltusrol wrote:

Karin:

So much for waiting the obligatory 72 hours, 36 will have to do.

I'm the guy you met in the parking lot. (You must remember my car.)
Short and sweet: when can I see you? I'm free when you're free. Probably
sooner.

(In a parking lot! Well at least neither of us was walking a dog.)

To: CNN/COMMENTS
From: Rob Baltusrol
Subj: Larry King

Larry, Larry, Larry:

The New York Times's recent front page story (on a Sunday, no less) on the alleged mistress of one George H. Bush (I'm talking the current president now, not his father's mistresses) was anything but a clear-cut example of liberal media bias. It of course was anything but. (Do you really not know how the game is played? You play it.)

It's called taking one for the team. It's called building consensus. So whenever the situation calls for invading foreign countries and killing their children Dick Cheney can go on Meet the Press, hold up a copy of the (liberal) New York Times and say, "If even the (liberal) New York Times says something must be done…." Well, then… Fire!

(To file under: What Should Have Been Painfully Obvious.)

Regards,

Rob Baltusrol

P.S. By the way, in the same show you used the expression, trying to get one of your guests to be more interesting/forthcoming, "two Jews talking." And I thought: how many stereotypes does that confirm?

To: karin@lotsalegs.com
From: Rob Baltusrol
Subj: archives

Since we're rummaging through old emails … gotta say: this might be my fave:

On 17 April 2007, at 18:25, rob baltusrol wrote:

Sheer poetry.

On 17 April 2007, at 18:22, karin@lotsalegs.com wrote:

when I was sucking your cock and you kept fingering me and rubbing my face then pulling me up and kissing me then pushing me back down.. my God.. I felt like this whore animal, in this fuck frenzy, I wanted your cock everywhere filling everything at once.

best fucking ever.. fuck fuck.

To: Maya Cekala
From: Rob Baltusrol
Subj: ahoy!

Hi Maya.

Was that you I saw walking down the street the other day?

From: Berkeley Cable Access
To: Rob Baltusrol
Subj: re: tech query

Rob Baltusrol--
We received your email, sorry about the delay. I checked with the most technically astute of our members and he said what you propose, linking all cable access stations nationally, might be feasible but would be a logistics nightmare. We find just reaching our own community to be all we can handle.

What did you have in mind?

On 30 March 2007, at 9:52, rob baltusrol wrote:

Hello Mr. Gostabel;

I was recently named program director for the Woodstock (NY) cable access television station. I read about your station, we seem to share similar philosophies (and budgets) and had a technical question: would it be possible, do you know, to link every cable access station in the country (for just an hour or so), so there might be a national cable access television show? Aired simultaneously nationwide?

Just curious.

Thanks for your time.

Rob Baltusrol

From: Andy Read
To: Rob Baltusrol
Subj: re: by jove!

Not totally?

What the fuck are you up to?

On 3 May 2007, at 11:02, rob baltusrol wrote:

Much.

I'd like to discuss this in person if that's all right. Not totally cloak-and-dagger, just would like to get your reaction. Thanks. Coffee? Tomorrow? (Is what's-her-name still working there?)

On 2 May 2007, at 12:52, andy read wrote:

Please, no.

It's better than the hairy yarmulkes for bald Jews idea, isn't it?

On 1 May 2007, at 19:02, rob baltusrol wrote:

I have an idea.

From: Claire Tansil
To: Rob Baltusrol
Subj:

Dear Rob. Thanks for sending me the 2 articles. Loved the Yard Sale one. Who has our Mousetrap game, anyway? Re: the pilot article, I'm not sure what the point is. Is he saying that someone else other than Islamic fundamentalists flew the planes into the towers? If so who? And why? Is he saying that it was not commercial airliners that were the weapons of destruction or that they were "military planes?" Or they actually were commercial airliners flown by experienced pilots (our own military or hey here's a thought, Mossad). Somehow, I get the feeling that Myers will somehow bring this around to that darn "Jewish problem" again. He might have some valid points to make but they are ultimately undermined by his thinly veiled anti-semitism. Yeah, yeah I know, *cui bono?* Love, Your sister

To: British-American Educational Foundation
From: Rob Baltusrol
Subj: re: annual directors' meeting

Wil;

Still staggered by the news, that we're only able to send one kid over next year. One?? (No year in Europe? What's this world coming to?)

There is a striking and unfortunate analogy, however: when I went over (30 of us!!) we traveled on the SS France — her last voyage as it turned out. (Best six consecutive days of my life.) Well I just read the very sad news that the SS France is to be broken up later this year. (Le Havre, Southampton, New York, Alang, India …)

Maybe we've been fighting off the wreckers too, Wil. Maybe it's time we asked: is it time to scuttle the ship?

(Even worse: hard to imagine you've outlived an ocean liner.)

On 28 April 2007, at 19:02, wil jeffries at baef.org wrote:

yes, sorry: annual board of directors meeting will be on Monday, 11 a.m., again in alex's offices. 441 lex., top floor. conference room. look forward to seeing all there. wil.

On 27 April 2007, at 10:10, david meacher at davidmeacher.com wrote:

Is there a BAEF board meeting monday? Have not heard anything since May 6 email.
Anyone?

Regards,

David

To: Sebastian Baltusrol
From: Rob Baltusrol
Subj: Come in London

Sebastian;

I know I mock the quality of education you're receiving in Savannah (maybe it was the certainty with which you said 12 feet are in a yard) so I thought the following passage in Hound of the Baskervilles might interest you, in which Watson (the good doctor) writes Holmes (a famous detective) from the misty moor:

"All this is foreign, however, to the mission on which you sent me, and will probably be uninteresting to your severely practical mind. I can still remember your complete indifference as to whether the sun moved around the earth or the earth round the sun."

To which I say: Dear Sherlock: have I got a school system for you!

Seriously, dear son (still), please let me know what's up with college, what your plans are, etc., etc. (I.e., you are going, right? Right? *Right*?)

From: kooliekatering.com
To: Rob Baltusrol
Subj: re: that all jazz?

Hi Robert;
I spoke with Len. He says you all were given a choice whether or not to keep working, and it was raining, so you all decided to go home. That's why no 4 hour minimum.
Let me know if you want to work at Hillcrest tomorrow. They need someone for the carving station. Thanx.
Suzanne

On 1 May 2007, at 14:44, rob baltusrol wrote:

Suzanne;

Got the jazz festival check, thanks: but $23?? I thought there was a four-hour minimum. That was a rainy, shitty Sunday night, it was supposed to be a 7-hour shift, I absolutely would not have gone out for that. (Not with Aunt Jess in Cabot Cove.)

Was there a mistake? Thanks.

Rob

On 20 April 2007, at 11:52, kooliekatering.com wrote:

Robert,
Lonnie just called, wanted to make a point of saying how you saved Saturday night, how grateful Evelyn was. (Where'd you learn to make a 30 minute crème brule?) Thanks again.
Suzanne

To: kooliekatering.com
From: Rob Baltusrol
Subj: re: that all jazz?

Suzanne;

That is absolutely not how it went down. It started raining, they told us to go home. End of story. (Where we were doing the dishes, it was mostly protected.) Please follow up on that.

Carving station? At a *high school*? (Tip jar?)

I actually sent these guys a letter not too long ago, pitched them teaching a writing/English composition/Shakespeare course. But sure, I'll carve their meat.

Rob

On 2 May 2007, at 9:49, kooliekatering.com wrote:

Hi Robert;
I spoke with Len. He says you all were given a choice whether or not to keep working, and it was raining, so you all decided to go home. That's why no 4 hour minimum.
Let me know if you want to work at Hillcrest tomorrow. They need someone for the carving station. Thanx.
Suzanne

On 1 May 2007, at 14:44, rob baltusrol wrote:

Suzanne;

Got the jazz festival check, thanks: but $23?? I thought there was a four-hour minimum. That was a rainy, shitty Sunday night, it was supposed to be a 7-hour shift, I absolutely would not have gone out for that. (Not with Aunt Jess in Cabot Cove.)

Was there a mistake? Thanks.

Rob

22

To: Helen Wicker
From: Rob Baltusrol
Subj: bagpipes, please

Mom;

I know you think I'm just a sentimental old fool, it's not really true. (Though I have been known to listen to Mull of Kintyre with the repeat button on.)

But it is with great sadness (okay, sentiment) I inform you that the SS France, my SS France, the last of the great liners, the last liner built specifically for the North Atlantic run, whose very last voyage was enjoyed (!) by none other than your extremely well-educated son, will soon be broken up. Trashed. Discarded. Sold for scrap.

All those great ships, from the Aquatania, whose propeller had more beauty and grace and better lines than the upper decks of the Queen Mary Two (no joke: I've seen the photos), to the Mauretania, to the Normandie, to the Queen Mary, to lastly the SS France, all gone. Not even sunk. It says something very bad about humans that we'd choose to eliminate the finest things we've ever offered. Today, when what's considered first class means so little, compared to a time when steerage meant something.

Now. Back to Ave Maria.

From: notify@namesdatabase
To: Rob Baltusrol
Subj: Your message to Bindy Oswald

We just wanted to let you know that at 8:24 p.m. on 5-02-07 your message was delivered to Bindy Oswald. For reference the body of your message is included below. If Bindy Oswald decides to reply, the reply will be sent to this address.

Take care, The Names Database Team

Message:

Ah, Bindy;

I knew if I kept looking, I'd find you. I just didn't expect it to take 30 years.

#9, #9

To: Human Resources
From: Rob Baltusrol
Subj: Copywriter

To whom it may concern;

While the bulk of my working life has been spent in journalism and its fringes, as my resume shows, I have also written reams of ad and marketing copy for clients as diverse as Macy's ("Sofas and love seats meant for each other"), Crazy Eddie appliance stores ("Washington: the man, the bridge, the sale"), Wamsutta ("The rest is up to you"), and CBS Records ("The category is Sills," for guitarist Dwight Sills. (I never heard of him again either.))

More recent is "Life's Short. Vacations are Shorter." for a Key West travel agency I am loathe to identify because he is giving every indication of stiffing me.

I am able to start work immediately.

Thank you.

EXPERIENCE

EDITOR-AT-LARGE, Daily Freeman, Kingston, NY   **2005-2007**

Wrote articles and editorials; edited, proofed copy; took photographs; wrote *Kingston Diary*, a weekly about-town column. Originated story ideas, beats. Conceived special editorial supplements. *Germantown: Only in America*. First place, AP 2005. Did layout; did everything.

STORE MANAGER, Archaic Books, Savannah, GA   **2002-2004**

Ran Savannah's oldest used book store. Appraised and purchased books, including scarce first editions. Dealt with customers, money; organized regular public events, including book signings and readings by local authors. Hired, trained, and evaluated personnel. Read *Finnegans Wake*.

PRODUCER, WJCT-TV, Savannah, GA   **1996-2001**

Produced five weekend broadcasts, working from in-house reports, network feeds, and AP wires. Wrote, edited, approved all scripts; wrote, produced own segments, including *Savannah Nights*, broadcast nationally. Adept at all the nitty-gritty: live shots, breaking news, election night.

MANAGING EDITOR, East Hampton Star, East Hampton, NY **1995**

From: karin@lotsalegs.com
To: Rob Baltusrol
Subj: re: archives

mine.

On 8 April 2007, at 12:27, rob baltusrol wrote:

Fuck me harder you fucker wasn't bad, either. (Make up your mind...)

On 8 April 2007, at 12:23, rob baltusrol wrote:

Words I'll never forget: *Stop ... fucking ... me.* (Never sounded so good.)

On 8 April 2007, at 11:33, karin@lotsalegs.com wrote:

favorite moment: Saturday morning, in our robes, in the kitchen.
you came over, holding your coffee, and you leaned down and
brushed my robe aside and put your hand on my pussy and said: I
plan on giving this a good workout this weekend. I hope you're
alright with that... my God! mush!

From: Tia Waller/Malvernian Society
To: Rob Baltusrol
Subj: re: Come in Malvern

Hello again ---
We are delighted that you want to get back in touch with us again and are
very pleased to help in any way we can. You will understand that we have
to be a bit careful when it comes to giving out contact details of OMs. If
there is someone in particular that you would like to contact, then please
let us know and we will contact them first before sending out their details.
The same goes for any Ellerslie contacts. How carefully their records have
been kept, we are not sure, as they are not in this office, but we could
inquire for you.
The long room is still there but is no longer the sixth form bar, which has
moved to St. Edmunds Hall.
The College is looking beautiful today, clear crisp day with long shadows
across the grass.
With very best wishes,
Tia Waller
Malvernian Society, Malvern College.

On 19 April 2007, at 18:25, rob baltrusrol wrote:

Hello Tia.

I'm an old alum. (Those records probably no longer exist.)

One idea for your website: is there a page with OM's email addresses?
That would be a big help. So many I'd like to say hello to. (Not as good as
the pub idea, but still... Speaking of which -- is there still the Long Room?
Long House? The school pub overlooking the cricket pitch?)

Also: any way to get in touch with someone from Ellerslie, before, long
before, it merged with Malvern? Any email addresses available there?
(Yes, an old fling.)
School looks great. One of these days …

Rob Baltusrol

To: Allison Hirst
From: Rob Baltusrol
Subj: Even Siberia Goes Through the Motions

Yeah. Good old Erica. Not much of a writer, not much of an editor, not much with original story ideas either, and don't know that she knows how to operate a camera. But when it comes to offering a house for a baby shower, or cooking a meal for an employee with a sick mum — look out! She's your gal! (Is there a greater newsroom skill?)

And thanks for that Youtube link, Allison. I saw Yes at Wembley, years ago. With Seals and Croft, if you can believe that.

On 3 May 2007, at 11:51, twoginsshaken@bellsouth.net wrote:

Did you see who they named editor?

From: Joanna Wallen
To: Rob Baltusrol
Subj: re: Family Docs

Will let you know. Thanx.
Joanna.

On 28 April 2007, at 19:32, rob baltusrol wrote:

Joanna;

It was nice meeting you the other day, seeing your shop and meeting your great-grandfather, hearing some of his tales. And belatedly it has occurred to me: I run a side business: shooting family documentaries, documentaries of everyday families. You may have seen my ad: You Are the Story. (Subhead: Families … It's where the action is.)

Included with the documentary is a questionnaire, some sample questions are below. I thought your grandfather might enjoy taking a look. Cheers.

Rob Baltusrol

1. What is your all-time favorite residence? (Address.)

2. What album has provided you with the most hours of listening pleasure?

3. What do you believe is the truest thing ever said?

4. Are you more or less comforted by a conspicuous police presence?

5. Have you ever shoplifted?

6. What's the most valuable course you ever took, college or high school?

7. Have you ever flown Pan Am?

8. About what action taken in your life do you most wish someone had urged you to reconsider?

9. Which color property do you prefer owning in Monopoly?

10. Have you ever seen a ghost?

To: Allison Hirst
From: Rob Baltusrol
Subj: re: editor

Another office lesson: beware the person who doesn't have a kind word to say about anyone, but about whom not an unkind word is said. That's the one you always watch for. (That's Barzini!)

On 3 May 2007, at 11:51, twoginsshaken@bellsouth.net wrote:

Did you see who they named editor?

From: British-American Educational Foundation
To: Rob Baltusrol
Subj: re: Some view

spoke to Natalie. she does know those people. they remember you.

will.

On 3 May 2007, at 10:14, rob baltusrol wrote:

By the way, can't believe Natalie lives across the street from the El
Dorado. I lived in the penthouse there — duplex, two terraces. Did she tell
you? Unbelievable. Faye Dunaway lived below me — about 20 stories
below. She used to get off the elevator, I'd wave. She'd walk off shaking
her head.

On 28 April 2007, at 19:02, wil jeffries at baef.org wrote:

yes, sorry: annual board of directors meeting will be on
Monday, 11 a.m., again in alex's offices. 441 lex., top floor.
conference room. look forward to seeing all there. wil.

On 27 April 2007, at 10:10, david meacher at davidmeacher.com
wrote:

Is there a BAEF board meeting monday? Have not heard anything
since May 6 email.
Anyone?

Regards,

David

From: Public/NYT/NYTIMES
To: Rob Baltusrol
Subj: re: usual lies

Thank you for contacting the Public Editor. An associate or I read every message. Because of the volume of e-mail, we cannot respond personally to every message, but we forward many messages to appropriate newsroom staffers and follow up to be sure concerns raised in those messages are treated with serious consideration. If a further reply is warranted, you will be hearing from us shortly.

Requests for corrections should be submitted to nytnews@nytimes.com. If you are dissatisfied with the response, please let us know.

When referring to a specific article, please include its date, section and headline.

To: public@nytimes
From: Rob Basltusrol
Subj: usual lies

Editor;

Push, huh?

That's the word you used to describe what would happen to office furniture if a jetliner crashed into a building — furniture would be "pushed" against the wall. Not scattered? Everywhere? Obliterated even?

But that's not the image the Times wanted to convey (so many images, the twin towers): the Times wanted to convey the image of *people* pushing the furniture against the wall, as if getting ready for a sock hop. Why? Because when people push furniture against a wall the furniture is placed together — better for dancing, better for burning. Correct?

And "meticulous"; "comprehensive"; "precise"; "robust" … I haven't seen so many power words since I threw together my last resume. (What? No "rigorous"?)

Keep up the good work.

Rob Baltusrol

To: Claire Tansil
From: Rob Baltusrol
Subj: re:

Dear Claire;

Thanks for the email, thanks for reading the article.

A couple of points: one doesn't have to have an alternative theory to find a presented theory implausible. I don't have to know who a woman is to know she's not Sophia Loren. And all he's saying is simple: people without flying experience could no more fly a commercial jet than you or I could perform open heart surgery. (Who has Operation?)

As for the Pentagon plane, it's even simpler: the government says the plane that hit the Pentagon flew at a height of 20 feet for approximately a mile. Why? Because telephone wires a mile from the Pentagon were, according to the government, brought down by the plane. So: very simple. Let's see if a commercial jet that size can fly for a mile at 20 feet. If it can't, as the author, a pilot, attests, then that part of the government's explanation is hogwash. And from what I've read, it all is.

(Interesting too that black boxes should vanish while a passport appears. Such a day!!)

On 2 May 2007, at 13:11, claire tansil wrote:

Dear Rob. Thanks for sending me the 2 articles. Loved the Yard Sale one. Who has our Mousetrap game, anyway? Re: the pilot article, I'm not sure what the point is. Is he saying that someone else other than Islamic fundamentalists flew the planes into the towers? If so who? And why? Is he saying that it was not commercial airliners that were the weapons of destruction or that they were "military planes?" Or they actually were commercial airliners flown by experienced pilots (our own military or hey here's a thought, Mossad). Somehow, I get the feeling that Myers will somehow bring this around to that darn "Jewish problem" again. He might have some valid points to make but they are ultimately undermined by his thinly veiled anti-semitism. Yeah, yeah I know, *cui bono?* Love, Your sister

From: Marcello Robertson
To: Rob Baltusrol
Subj: re: Bad Rice

```
I'm very interested in reading your
script. Please snail mail
a copy to my office, also include a
release form with that script.
```

-----Original Message-----
From: malvern [mailto:malvern@legacy.net]
Sent: Monday, March 23, 2007 7:58 AM
To: marcello@robertson-entertainment.com
Subject: BAD RICE

LOGLINE AND SYNOPSIS FOR 'BAD RICE'

LOGLINE: Racist cop gets bumped in the head, suffers
amnesia, ends up working at a black bar.

SYNOPSIS:
White bartender, black bar.
That was the original idea behind the screenplay 'Bad Rice.'
Then the bartender became a cop, then a cop who had amnesia
who forgot he was a racist. Once there were some murders the
local news got involved, so too the world's youngest felon,
then a colleague of the bartender's just looking for a young
felon to kill.
'Bad Rice' is a dark farce, a cross between Pulp Fiction and
(Altman's) M*A*S*H. Its theme is race, most every page. Live
in the south for even a short time, and you soon realize: race is
everything. Every conversation, every suggestion, every look
at a passerby is somehow corrupted by race. 'Bad Rice'
exploits that, articulating what are usually kept as thoughts,
while exposing both societies, the ghettoed and the gated. It is
also, I think, very, very funny.
Specifically, the screenplay has to do with two crimes, one in a
rural area of the south (93rd market), one in a metropolitan
area. It ridicules the two groups that enjoy it least: the media
and law enforcement. It has to do with the friendship between
the world's ugliest and best-looking black men, and it has to do
with one cop's struggle to make good, and do the right thing.
To at least remember that.

From: Andy Read
To: Rob Baltusrol
Subj: re:

Cind says hi. Wants to know if you're seeing anyone.

On 4 May 2007, at 23:31, rob baltusrol wrote:

And what do they say? After 50 feet, a fall's a fall?

Thanks, pal. Terrific.

On 4 May 2007, at 23:11, andy read wrote:

Rob,

You are not going to believe this.

Courtesy of Cindy (Cind who loves you, but ….) we go to the pictures last night. She asks how you are, what we talked about… you know. The usual interrogation. I hem and haw.

So the trailers start, we look toward the screen: and it's the World Trade Center. The twin towers, Rob, it was a doc on that guy that walked between them, little Philipe. One moment it was an idea, he said, the next he knew he was testing the rope.

So I turned to Cind and I said, Well, Rob has this idea…..

(It's a hell of a height, pal!)

LOVE UR GUTS

Andy

To: Andy Read
From: Rob Baltusrol
Subj: re: joice

I am as a matter of fact, we just met. Recently.

On 4 May 2007, at 23:31, andy read wrote:

Cind says hi. Wants to know if you're seeing anyone.

On 4 May 2007, at 23:22, rob baltusrol wrote:

And what do they say? After 50 feet, a fall's a fall?

Thanks, pal. Terrific.

On 4 May 2007, at 23:11, andy read wrote:

Rob,

You are not going to believe this.

Courtesy of Cindy (Cind who loves you, but ....) we go to the pictures last night. She asks how you are, what we talked about… you know. The usual interrogation. I hem and haw.

So the trailers start, we look toward the screen: and it's the World Trade Center. The twin towers, Rob, it was a doc on that guy that walked between them, little Philipe. One moment it was an idea, he said, the next he knew he was testing the rope.

So I turned to Cind and I said, Well, Rob has this idea…..

(It's a hell of a height, pal!)

LOVE UR GUTS

Andy

To: karin@lotsalegs.com
From: Rob Baltusrol
Subj: Archives III

Oh! I almost forgot.

On 6 April 2007, at 18:41, rob baltusrol wrote:

No matter how many times you hear it…

On 6 April 2007, at 15:44, karin@lotsalegs.com wrote:

by the way, your some kisser. and that's some great cock.

To: Andy Read
From: Rob Baltusrol
Subj: re: joice

We fuck we fuck we fuck we fuck, she's the greatest thing in the world.

On 4 May 2007, at 23:35, andy read wrote:

????

On 4 May 2007, at 23:34, rob baltusrol wrote:

I am as a matter of fact, we just met. Recently.

On 4 May 2007, at 23:31, andy read wrote:

Cind says hi. Wants to know if you're seeing anyone.

On 4 May 2007, at 23:22, rob baltusrol wrote:

And what do they say? After 50 feet, a fall's a fall?

Thanks, pal. Terrific.

On 4 May 2007, at 23:11, andy read wrote:

Rob,

You are not going to believe this.

Courtesy of Cindy (Cind who loves you, but ....) we go to the pictures last night. She asks how you are, what we talked about… you know. The usual interrogation. I hem and haw.

So the trailers start, we look toward the screen: and it's the World Trade Center. The twin towers, Rob, it was a doc on that guy that walked between them, little Philipe. One moment it was an idea, he said, the next he knew he was testing the rope.

To: Andy Read
From: Rob Baltusrol
Subj: re: joice

As long as there's a working fireplace...

On 4 May 2007, at 23:35, andy read wrote:

????

On 4 May 2007, at 23:34, rob baltusrol wrote:

I am as a matter of fact, we just met. Recently.

On 4 May 2007, at 23:31, andy read wrote:

Cind says hi. Wants to know if you're seeing anyone.

On 4 May 2007, at 23:22, rob baltusrol wrote:

And what do they say? After 50 feet, a fall's a fall?

Thanks, pal. Terrific.

On 4 May 2007, at 23:11, andy read wrote:

Rob,

You are not going to believe this.

Courtesy of Cindy (Cind who loves you, but ....) we go to the pictures last night. She asks how you are, what we talked about... you know. The usual interrogation. I hem and haw.

So the trailers start, we look toward the screen: and it's the World Trade Center. The twin towers, Rob, it was a doc on that guy that walked between them, little Philipe. One moment it was an idea, he said, the next he knew he was testing the rope.

From: Claire Tansil
To: Rob Baltusrol
Subj:

Rob;

And I'm sorry, but I just don't see why you always have to be doing this, tearing down your country, a country that has been so good to you and given you so much. Why? What have you given it? Yeah, the government that paid for the birth of your child, you mean? Do you even pay taxes?

Givers and takers, Rob. Givers and takers.

Claire

To: Grayson Galleries
From: Rob Baltusrol
Subj: sad news

Miranda;

I've been having no luck sending JC an email, so went online and very sad
to have to find his obituary. Here it is, I thought you'd want to read it.

http://www.virginislandsdailynews.com/index/lanigan

Remember the Christmas miracle? How for the first few weeks in
Portugal the fireplace wouldn't work, I tried raising the grate, I even
banged off some of the chimney up on the roof. Still, every night, all
smoke. Then we were invited in town for Christmas dinner (Bea and ....
Ulph?). And we went home and I said, what the hell, give it one more try,
threw some wood in there, lit it -- and up the chimney went the smoke and
we didn't have a problem with it since. (Dean Martin's Let It Snow Let It
Snow Let It Snow playing on transistor Portuguese radio, if memory
serves, and you know it does.)

From: British-American Educational Foundation
To: Rob Baltusrol
Subj: re: outgoogled

onwards & upwards!

incidentally, some members made comments on your wardrobe after the meeting. Think it might be a good idea for next time to wear a tie. wil.

On 3 May 2007, at 21:22, rob baltusrol wrote:

Dear Fellow Board Members (FBM's):

Good news, bad news.

The bad news is: when one googles BAEF, the Belgian American Educational Fund comes first.

Good news is we continue to beat out the Bulgarian-American Enterprise Fund.

To: Sebastian Baltusrol
From: Rob Baltusrol
Subj: going once ... going twice...

Sebastian ... Sebastian ... Sebastian ... Sebastian ...

(I found $400 on the street yesterday. I have no idea what to do with it.

Any ideas?)

To: British-American Educational Foundation
From: Rob Baltusrol
Subj: re: outgoogled

Wil;

Re: the tie: yes, the thought did occur to me. But I also thought, since this was a meeting only amongst ourselves, in a board room, not even at the Yale Club (*what happened to the Yale Club?!?*), what harm was there that one us should come out of the woods to attend. But point taken. Thanks. (At least I left my ax at home.)

Rob

On 5 May 2007, at 10:29, wil jeffries at baef.org wrote:

onwards & upwards!

incidentally, some members made comments on your wardrobe after the meeting. Think it might be a good idea for next time to wear a tie. wil.

On 3 May 2007, at 21:22, rob baltusrol wrote:

Dear Fellow Board Members (FBM's):

Good news, bad news.

The bad news is: when one googles BAEF, the Belgian American Educational Fund comes first.

Good news is we continue to beat out the Bulgarian-American Enterprise Fund.

To: Morton Library
From: Rob Baltusrol
Subj: re: reminder

Dear Charlis;

Two more days! Max. Promise.

(And whatever happened to Kathleen Byron??)

-----Original Message-----
From: morton library
Sent to: Rob Baltusrol
Subject: Best of Film noir
Date: March 12 2007

Hi Rob;

Just a reminder: you still have the classic film noir DVD.

(Didn't you already see this?)

To: Claire Tansil
From: Rob Baltusrol
Subj: Whoa Nellie!

Well, that was a jump. How long has that been building up?

I love you dearly, Claire, and yes, there's a big but coming: BUT you have never been able to think for yourself. Ask yourself: why *haven't* we seen footage of the Pennsylvania air crash? Doesn't that strike you as a little odd? We've seen footage from every other airplane crash in the world. (No tail section? There's *always* a tail section.)

Yes, this country has given me a lot (and whoever came up with the idea of unemployment insurance I owe a big thank you). But this country ain't that country, Claire. And Donald Rumsfeld and Dick Cheney are not nice people but Americans are too busy waving the flag to notice. (Have you ever seen so many flags? Did Nazi Germany have as many swastikas?) (Every subway car in New York?? Whose decision was that!?) The flag's gotten in your eyes, Claire. I suggest you remove it, look around. It's not a pretty sight. (More flags!!!)

And *thinly-veiled anti-Semitism?!?* Where on earth did you get that? No mention of Jews, no mention of Israel, no mention of Mossad. Just a (very) dry treatise on aeronautics.

(Oh well... at least it wasn't virulent.)

Your pesky bro.

On 4 May 2007, at 14:26, claire tansil wrote:

Rob;

And I'm sorry, but I just don't see why you always have to be doing this, tearing down your country, a country that has been so good to you and given you so much. Why? What have you given it? Yeah, the government that paid for the birth of your child, you mean? Do you even pay taxes?

Givers and takers, Rob. Givers and takers.

Claire

From: Sebastian Baltusrol
To: Rob Baltusrol
Subj: re: going once ... going twice ...

hi dad

sorry it's been awhile, busy busy. But, uh, about college..

--the $400 was a joke, right?--

On 2 May 2007, at 9:52, rob baltusrol wrote:

Sebastian ... Sebastian ... Sebastian ... Sebastian ...

(Oh! I found $400 on the street yesterday. I have no idea what to do with
it.

Any ideas?)

From: British-American Educational Foundation
To: Rob Baltusrol
Subj: re: cold alum

no, it certainly wasn't. after you left (he was the year after you at Malvern) he was telling us some of the stories. safe to say none of us had your year.

he said you almost got thrown out, and lost your scholarship... did you lose your scholarship? was Madeleine aware of all that?
wil.

On 3 May 2007, at 21:49, rob baltusrol wrote:

Wil;

By the way: what was the deal with that Robert guy? The new member? Awful sullen. I tried getting him to talk but kept giving me the brush off. And he went to Malvern! (What kind of year did he have? Certainly not the year I had.)

To: karin@lotsalegs.com
From: Rob Baltusrol
Subj: re: gale

By the way, the two best blowjobs I ever received were from you, back to back. (Hey: let's try that!) Saturday night, in front of the fire (chestnuts roasting), then in bed, Sunday morning. (Lordy, lordy.)

On 4 May 2007, at 22:30, karin@lotsalegs.com wrote:

how'd you like to swap one of those blow jobs for a massage?

 -Pussy Galore

From: karin@lotsalegs.com
To: Rob Baltusrol
Subj: re: gale

why lil ol' me? she replies blushing. (i knew i was good, but..)

What makes a good blowjob anyway?

On 5 May 2007, at 12:50, rob baltusrol wrote:

By the way, the two best blowjobs I ever received were from you, back to back. (Hey: let's try that!) Saturday night, in front of the fire (chestnuts roasting), then in bed, Sunday morning. (Lordy, lordy.)

On 4 May 2007, at 22:30, karin@lotsalegs.com wrote:

how'd you like to swap one of those blow jobs for a massage?

 -Pussy Galore

To: British-American Educational Foundation
From: Rob Baltusrol
Subj: re: cold alum

Well, in my defense (never said that before!) I also got a letter from the guy who went two years after me, and it was far from critical. And he said they also were still talking about me. And I believe the phrase he used (actually, I know; I still have the letter) was that I was looked upon as some kind of mythical American legend. (His words.)

So it wasn't all bad, Wil.

On 5 May 2007, at 12:59, wil jeffries at baef.org wrote:

no, it certainly wasn't. After you left (he was the year after you at Malvern) he was telling us some of the stories. Safe to say none of us had your year.

he said you almost got thrown out, and lost your scholarship... Did you lose your scholarship? Was Madeleine aware of all that?
wil.

On 3 May 2007, at 21:49, rob baltusrol wrote:

Wil;

By the way: what was the deal with that Robert guy? The new member? Awful sullen. I tried getting him to talk but kept giving me the brush off. And he went to Malvern! (What kind of year did he have? Certainly not the year I had.)

From: Andy Read
To: Rob Baltusrol
Subj: re: forgot to ask

I like it..

On 5 May 2007, at 11:50, rob baltusrol wrote:

To me, the biggest mystery of 9/11 — other than building 7; other than the plane that disappeared into the Pentagon; other than the plane that disappeared in Pennsylvania; other than … — is: why four planes? Why so many, or why separate targets? Obviously the World Trade Center was going to be your visual: so why not do everything to guarantee that visual? Especially since there was no guarantee that a, any of the planes would hit their target, and b, would bring the tower(s) down. (Putting aside the fact any number of planes couldn't do it.) Why even bother with Washington and wherever the Pennsylvania plane was heading?

And the answer is obviously that the planes weren't needed to bring the buildings down. (Watson! Come quick!) But also: think 9/11, what do you think? The towers, right? Then the Pentagon, then the plane in Pennsylvania, then your mind goes back to the towers, right? What the Pentagon plane (and Pennsylvania) serve as are distractions, forcing us to look away just as the magician pockets the coin. And when we look back at NY — too late, it's gone.

What's gone!?!?!

On 5 May 2007, at 10:41, andy read wrote:

I never asked: what's you take on 9/11? Any theories?

To: karin@lotsalegs.com
From: Rob Baltusrol
Subj: re: gale

Duration.

On 5 May 2007, at 12:52, karin@lotsalegs.com wrote:

why lil ol' me? she replies blushing. (i knew i was good, but..)

What makes a good blowjob anyway?

On 5 May 2007, at 12:50, rob baltusrol wrote:

By the way, the two best blowjobs I ever received were from you, back to
back. (Hey: let's try that!) Saturday night, in front of the fire (chestnuts
roasting), then in bed, Sunday morning. (Lordy, lordy.)

On 4 May 2007, at 22:30, karin@lotsalegs.com wrote:

how'd you like to swap one of those blow jobs for a
massage?

 -Pussy Galore

From: British-American Educational Foundation
To: Rob Baltusrol
Subj: re: cold alum

not sure that was quite the legend they had in mind when they sent you over.

wil.

On 5 May 2007, at 13:14, rob baltusrol wrote:

Well, in my defense (never said that before!) I also got a letter from the guy who went two years after me, and it was far from critical. And he said they also were still talking about me. And I believe the phrase he used (actually, I know; I still have the letter) was that I was looked upon as some kind of mythical American legend. (His words.)

So it wasn't all bad, Wil.

On 5 May 2007, at 12:59, wil jeffries at baef.org wrote:

no, it certainly wasn't. After you left (he was the year after you at Malvern) he was telling us some of the stories. Safe to say none of us had your year.

he said you almost got thrown out, and lost your scholarship... Did you lose your scholarship? Was Madeleine aware of all that?

wil.

On 3 May 2007, at 21:49, rob baltusrol wrote:

Wil;

By the way: what was the deal with that Robert guy? The new member. Awful sullen. I tried getting him to talk but kept giving me the brush off. And he went to Malvern! (What kind of year did he have? Certainly not the year I had.)

He lost his virginity to Jackie Onassis.

OR

His claim to fame was that he slept with both Jackie Onassis and Princess Di.

He said he met Jackie in Hyannis Port while working for Ethel Kennedy, whom he loathed. Jackie used to drop by unannounced and stay at Jack's old house. First time he saw her she was down at the beach talking to Rose Kennedy, who was wearing rain gear at the time, despite it being a clear, sunny day. And he said she looked much better in person, much. Jackie, that is. Not Rose.

"And she asked if I'd come by that night, help her with something in the kitchen, I forget what," he said. "And that was that."

He was 20 then, and about 20 years later he met Di.

"I was working for a local paper in the Hamptons, managing editor," (the editor was a lot like Ethel, he said), "and she was a guest at some estate." She accepted his request for an interview, he said, and when he went over he discovered they were alone. "She opened the door for me herself," he said. "Just like they always say they do."

"And there again, it was the kitchen. I tell ya, for me, kitchens are where it's at."

I asked him why he was telling me this and he said, "Because you mentioned them both in the same sentence. And for years I've been waiting for that, for someone to touch the magic brick that leads to the hidden staircase."

He signaled the bartender.

"And because it's a good secret," he said. "And secrets have to be let out once in awhile, and allowed to run around. Or else they die."

From: kooliekatering.com
To: Rob Baltusrol
Subj: Hillcrest shift

Robert--

We've received a complaint from Hillcrest. They accuse you of excessive fraternization with the students, females, especially. And two teachers said you took it upon yourself to engage in what they believed was a private conversation, offering an opinion where none was asked for.

This is not what you were there for. You were there to prepare and serve food, only. Nothing else.

Suzanne

To: kooliekatering.com
From: Rob Baltusrol
Subj: re: Hillcrest shift

Suzanne;

First things first: The guy misattributed a famous Shakespeare quote.
What was I expected to do? (Hamlet may have agreed all the world's a
stage, but he didn't say it.)

As for being too friendly... can I help it if the students are polite? Am I
not supposed to say "You're welcome" to every student who thanks me?
(Should I ignore the polite, pretty girls?)

And what about that in-house nun -- too nice there too? Should I have told
her to go to hell?

On 5 May 2007, at 16:29, kooliekatering.com wrote:

Robert--
We've received a complaint from Hillcrest. They accuse you of
excessive fraternization with the students, females, especially. And
two teachers said you took it upon yourself to engage in what they
believed was a private conversation, offering an opinion where
none was asked for.
This is not what you were there for. You were there to prepare and
serve food, only. Nothing else.
Suzanne

From: notify@namesdatabase
To: Rob Baltusrol
Subj: Your message to Bindy Oswald

We just wanted to let you know that at 8:24 p.m. on 5-02-07 your message was delivered to Bindy Oswald. For reference the body of your message is included below. If Bindy Oswald decides to reply, the reply will be sent to this address.

Take care, The Names Database Team

Message:

Bindy;

I don't know if you ever got my first note, this site seems more con than connection. So in case you didn't, it is me, Rob. That Rob.

And if you did get my message, and for whatever very good reason choose not to respond, I beg you to at least answer me this: do you have a daughter that looks just like you, and would she have had cause to have been in Amsterdam a couple of years ago? (December 2002, to be exact.) I was in a coffee shop there when "she" entered, but for some reason was incapable of going over and asking.

And I hope I'm not getting her in trouble. Coming from someone, to someone, who know all about that…

Me

From: Andy Read
To: Rob Baltusrol
Subj: re:

You make it seem so easy.

On 5 May 2007, at 13:42, rob baltusrol wrote:

You know what this is about, And? You're going to think I'm crazy, but I really think this is true. And even I didn't know it till now.

Years ago, more than 25 years ago (!), I had a date with a girl named Adrian, a real looker. One date. That was it. We went our separate ways. Never to see each other again.

Except: last year, I got back in touch with her. She was surprised to say the least. ("*Who*?") But she was class all the way even if she suspected something was up, and what was up was that my life was falling apart. (No comments, please.) I had control over nothing so decided to take control over something and that was to get in touch with a girl I otherwise would never have crossed paths with again. Done.

I was just taking action, I was changing history. My own at first.

It was a prelude.

To: kooliekatering.com
From: Rob Baltusrol
Subj: re: Hillcrest shift

Oh, I'll get by Suzanne, (though I'll certainly miss Gummy Bear Day).

And I'll give you one week to pay me the four hours for the jazz festival, that's it. One week, or it's small claims court.

Women have nothing on this guy scorned…

On 5 May 2007, at 16:55, kooliekatering.com wrote:

I'm sorry, Robert. We can no longer use you. Suzanne

On 5 May 2007, at 16:42, rob baltusrol wrote:

Suzanne;

First things first: The guy misattributed a famous Shakespeare quote. What was I expected to do? (Hamlet may have agreed all the world's a stage, but he didn't say it.)

As for being too friendly… can I help it if the students are polite? Am I not supposed to say "You're welcome" to every student who thanks me? (Should I ignore the polite, pretty girls?)

And what about that in-house nun -- too nice there too? Should I have told her to go to hell?

On 5 May 2007, at 16:29, kooliekatering.com wrote:

Robert--
We've received a complaint from Hillcrest. They accuse you of excessive fraternization with the students, females, especially. And two teachers said you took it upon yourself to engage in what they believed was a private conversation, offering an opinion where none was asked for.

To: Andy Read
From: Rob Baltusrol
Subj: re: birth

It is easy. We'll look back and it'll look impossible and we'll have
forgotten how easy it was.

Trust me.

On 5 May 2007, at 22:52, andy read wrote:

You make it seem so easy.

On 5 May 2007, at 13:42, rob baltusrol wrote:

You know what this is about, And? You're going to think I'm crazy, but I
really think this is true. And I didn't even know it till now.

Years ago, more than 25 years ago (!), I had a date with a girl named
Adrian, a real looker. One date. That was it. We went our separate ways.
Never to see each other again.

Except: last year, I got back in touch with her. She was surprised to say the
least. ("*Who*?") But she was class all the way even if she suspected
something was up, and what was up was that my life was falling apart.
(No comments, please.) I had control over nothing so decided to take
control over something, and that was to get in touch with a girl I otherwise
would never have crossed paths with again. Done.

I was just taking action, I was changing history. My own at first.

It was a prelude.

To: Mike Powers/WoodstockTV
From: Rob Baltusrol
Subj: re: last night

Israel is the problem.

(What's with the font, Mike?)

On 6 May 2007, at 9:42, Mike Powers <woodstockpublictv.org> wrote:

am I hearing this right?? in last night's program you said israel was the problem?

To: Mike Powers/WoodstockTV
From: Rob Baltustrol
Subj: minutes by minutes

Just out of curiosity: is this how monthly meetings normally work? You all get together, discuss everything that was discussed at the last meeting, say goodnight, then do it all over again in 30 days?

On 6 May 2007, at 9:42, Mike Powers <woodstockpublictv.org> wrote:

am I hearing this right? in last night's program you said israel was the problem?

To: Sebastian Baltusrol
From: Rob Baltusrol
Subj: re: going once ... going twice ...

Sebastian:

I'm not in the mood: what about college?

On 5 May 2007, at 13:11, sebastian baltusrol wrote:

hi dad

sorry it's been awhile, busy busy. But, uh, about college..

--the $400 was a joke, right?--

On 2 May 2007, at 9:52, rob baltusrol wrote:

Sebastian ... Sebastian ... Sebastian ... Sebastian ...

(Oh! I found $400 on the street yesterday. I have no idea what to do with
it.

Any ideas?)

From: karin@lotsalegs.com
To: Rob Baltusrol
Subj:

umm.. you do know I'm jewish, right?

To: karin@lotsalegs.com
From: Rob Baltusrol
Subj: What!?!

Birnbaum?

Not Greek?

On 6 May 2007, at 12:12, karin@lotsalegs.com wrote:

umm.. you do know I'm jewish, right?

To: Andy Read
From: Rob Baltusrol
Subj: it's a pageant!

And;

Remember White Christmas? Wherein those masters of the slopes, Bing
Crosby and Danny Kaye, have to get all their old Army pals up to the
woods for one final salute to crusty former general, Dean Jagger. What's
the only way to mobilize the troops?

Easy. Go on TV.

Same thing here. der Bingle was handed the mic, we're seizing it.

Rebellions do it all the time.

To: Charles Wilcon
From: Rob Baltusrol
Subj: re:

Chas! Is it you?!? Lad? (Or was it mate?)

So damn good to hear from you! How are you? Where are you? I wrote you awhile back (actually it was about 20 years ago) to your old Home Park Rd., Wimbledon address, but I gather you moved.

You're not gonna believe this, but guess what board I sit on? As in board of directors. The British-American Educational Foundation! (Irony enters a new dimension.) The same outfit that sent me over and nearly threw me out. (And they never even knew what Bindy and I were up to.)

I tell you, Chas: when I went over, there were 30 of us. That's 30 schools! A reception was held for us in New York before we went, someone had to book passage for all of us to sail over, get train tickets from Southampton to London, book hotel rooms for us that night; transportation had to be arranged to each of our various schools; someone thought to organize a Thanksgiving dinner for us at some hotel in London, there were excursions throughout the year, many of us went to Venice during our spring break, arranged by the London director …

Now, we sit around our conference table with our lame plate of sandwiches, barely able to send one kid over a year (by plane) and I think: so this is what's become of adults.

Anyway, Chas, please: let me know what's up. Any booze-ups?

And … of course … Chas: how is she? Any word?

(Have I got a story for you.)

On 6 May 2007, at 11:29, charles wilcon wrote:

Bloody Yank!

To: Riggs Plumbing Supply
From: Rob Baltusrol
Subj: bidets con't

Mills;

Or, we could always go with straight humor.

How about this for bidets, big headline:

FIRST THINGS FIRST

Rob

On 4 May 2007, at 19:02, rob baltusrol wrote:

Hello Mills.

I walked in off the street the other day, asked you some questions about
bidets, how many you sold, mentioned I did some advertising and would
you be interested if I came up with any ideas. You said yes. Well, I think I
have.

What do you think of this line:

Bidets. *A nice thing about civilization.*

I don't know if we'd use it on your website, or maybe we could run it in
the local paper. But I do think bidets in this country are something people
are ready to buy, just have to be nudged a little. Then it's, "Honey, call me
crazy, but you know what I'm thinking of buying…?" (Maybe *there's* our
line!)

Anyway, tell me what you think.

Rob

From: Andy Read
To: Rob Baltusrol
Subj:

Rob;

Thought you might appreciate this. (She gave her blessing.)

Andy

--- On **Tue, 5/3/07, 12:01 Andy Read <andyread@jetsons.com>** wrote:

For as long as I've known Rob, he's the greatest guy in the world, but fuck
him over and there's hell to pay. And that's how he's looking at it, I'm
sure. It doesn't matter if it's the government or anyone else. Rob doesn't
pick sides, he picks fights.

--- On **Tue, 5/3/07, 11:56 Cynthia Evenstock <12stepnurseries.com>**
wrote:

Does Rob ever frighten you? So righteous, so... angry, ??

To: Andy Read
From: Rob Baltusrol
Subj: re:

It's not business. It's strictly personal.

Thanks, And.

(*Angry* …???)

On 6 May 2007, at 19:55, andy read wrote:

Rob;

Thought you might appreciate this. (She gave her blessing.)

Andy

--- On **Tue, 5/3/07, 12:01 Andy Read <andyread@jetsons.com>** wrote:

For as long as I've known Rob, he's the greatest guy in the world, but fuck him over and there's hell to pay. And that's how he's looking at it, I'm sure. It doesn't matter if it's the government or anyone else. Rob doesn't pick sides, he picks fights.

--- On **Tue, 5/3/07, 11:56 Cynthia Evenstock <12stepnurseries.com>** wrote:

Does Rob ever frighten you? So righteous, so… angry, ??

To: karin@lotsalegs.com
From: Rob Baltusrol
Subj:

I can't wait to fuck you. I can't wait for you to walk through the door and drop to your knees and take my cock into that luscious mouth then stand you up and turn you around and lean you over the counter and repeatedly fuck that perfect pussy, that perfect ass.

Now: is it clear what awaits in Hurley?

From: Claire Tansil
To: Rob Baltusrol
Subj:

Swastikas, Rob? You're scaring me. What's next? Revolution? Storming
the gates? You're becoming the type we read about, that bomber in the
shack, shitting in the woods. Is that how you see yourself?

Forget about the country, Rob. What about you? Start smaller. Any
changes you could make there? Hey: here's a thought--why not a job?
What about going to work in the morning? Have you thought about that?
Too revolutionary? Getting a job? Paying your dues? Working for
something instead of always trying to find a shortcut. There's no such
thing as a free lunch, remember? Whose senior quote was that?
(Oh right. Yours!)
Claire

To: Mike Powers/WoodstockTV
From: Rob Baltusrol
Subj: re: last night

What about?

Mike: when I interviewed for this job, we all agreed: the purpose of public access TV was to air thoughts and opinions not expressed on mainstream, broadcast TV. And I think we can all agree that no thought is less expressed than Israel being the problem. Or, as ever, even on public access TV, is Israel the exception? (Talk about exceptionalism!)

I also said at the interview that if hired I would do everything I could to make Woodstock's public access television station the finest in the country. Didn't say I could do it, but said I would try. Mike: that's what I'm doing. As far as I'm concerned, I'm doing my job.

(And think of the ratings! We could be up to two dozen people by the end of the week!)

On 7 May 2007, at 8:50, Mike Powers <woodstockpublictv.org> wrote:

let's talk.

On 6 May 2007, at 9:48, rob baltusrol wrote:

Israel is the problem.

(What's with the font, Mike?)

On 6 May 2007, at 9:42, Mike Powers <woodstockpublictv.org> wrote:

am I hearing this right?? in last night's program you said israel was the problem?

From: Charles Wilcon
To: Rob Baltusrol
Subj:

Yes there was. In the hills, of course. Some miles back, a major boozeup.
Everyone it seemed, but you. Told stories though. Your first day, do you
remember? Walking up on that ridge, that hat you used to wear, all alone.
We were all looking at you, very cinemalike, and Richard~ remember
Richard? Always wore the sink stopper in his vest? Looked like a watch
chain? He turned and said, something tells me this is going to be a very
interesting year.

Then Chich~ remember Mark Chichester? (More beer nuts!) He told of the
time we were all at the rugger game and you had to go to the other side of
the pitch to talk to your housemaster about something so you started
walking the entire length of the field, Chich and I turned to watch you and
as we did saw everyone else watching the game turn to watch you too! We
both roared!

Some year, wasn't it?

To: Charles Wilcon
From: Rob Baltusrol
Subj: re: union

It sure was. And I remember you telling me that story. (Another lifetime indeed.)

But enough about Richard, enough about Chich:

Chas: Chas: was she?

On 6 May 2007, at 12:11, charles wilcon wrote:

Yes there was. In the hills, of course. Some miles back, a major boozeup. Everyone it seemed, but you. Told stories though. Your first day, do you remember? Walking up on that ridge, that hat you used to wear, all alone. We were all looking at you, very cinemalike, and Richard~ remember Richard? Always wore the sink stopper in his vest? Looked like a watch chain? He turned and said, something tells me this is going to be a very interesting year.

Then Chich~ remember Mark Chichester? (More beer nuts!) He told of the time we were all at the rugger game and you had to go to the other side of the pitch to talk to your housemaster about something so you started walking the entire length of the field, Chich and I turned to watch you and as we did saw everyone else watching the game turn to watch you too! We both roared!

Some year, wasn't it?

To: Claire Tansil
From: Rob Baltusrol
Subj: re:

I've had jobs, Claire. Real jobs. Elevators and everything. I keep losing them. Why? Because the least welcome person in any newsroom in America is the best newsman in the joint. That you find such a thought inconceivable is the problem -- so does most of America. They think journalism means Watergate. It means Lotto. It means someone I've never heard of is getting a divorce.

There's no winning with you, Claire. None. I tell you I win a playwriting contest and you don't ask to read the play. (A one-act!!) (Such reviews!) (Your brother the actor! Another direction! Another career!) I ask you to fill out a questionnaire for a side project of mine, shooting family documentaries, so I can get a better idea of which questions work best -- do you send it back? Do you fill it out? Of course not. (*Have* you ever shoplifted, Claire?)

You just pretend I don't do these things because it fits in much better with the picture of your brother the bum. You're perfect little world, no other world exists, and I'm not in it. Your little diorama. Doesn't matter what I do. No room. That's where the fireplace goes.

On 5 May 2007, at 16:44, claire tansil wrote:

Swastikas, Rob? You're scaring me. What's next? Revolution? Storming the gates? You're becoming the type we read about, that bomber in the shack, shitting in the woods. Is that how you see yourself?

Forget about the country, Rob. What about you? Start smaller. Any changes you could make there? Hey: here's a thought--why not a job? What about going to work in the morning? Have you thought about that? Too revolutionary? Getting a job? Paying your dues? Working for something instead of always trying to find a shortcut. There's no such thing as a free lunch, remember? Whose senior quote was that?
(Oh right. Yours!)
Claire

From: Bill Torrey
To: Rob Baltusrol
Subj: Scouting Opportunities

Hello Rob;

Of course I remember you. You were quite right about Oli Jokinen, and I've repeated many times your advice about only drafting players with the letter 'k' in their name, unless the letters are ORR.

Unfortunately our staff is full at present, and we really don't hire scouts unless they have years of junior hockey experience, which I gather from your resume you lack. But it was good to hear from you again, and I wish you all the best.

Bill Torrey
President, Florida Panthers

From: Mike Powers/WoodstockTV
To: Rob Baltusrol
Subj: re: last night

As long as you feel good about yourself, Rob. That's the important thing.

And what do I tell the Albany Times? And the Herald-Record? Any thoughts on that?

On 7 May 2007, at 9:02, rob baltusrol wrote:

What about?

Mike: when I interviewed for this job, we all agreed: the purpose of public access TV was to air thoughts and opinions not expressed on mainstream, broadcast TV. And I think we can all agree that no thought is less expressed than Israel being the problem. Or, as ever, even on public access TV, is Israel the exception? (Talk about exceptionalism!)

I also said at the interview that if hired I would do everything I could to make Woodstock's public access television station the finest in the country. Didn't say I could do it, but said I would try. Mike: that's what I'm doing. As far as I'm concerned, I'm doing my job.

(And think of the ratings! We could be up to two dozen people by the end of the week!)

On 7 May 2007, at 8:50, Mike Powers <woodstockpublictv.org> wrote:

let's talk.

On 6 May 2007, at 9:48, rob baltusrol wrote:

Israel is the problem.

(What's with the font, Mike?)

To: Andy Read
From: Rob Baltusrol
Subj: yee-hi!

And we're off!

Hey: remember when Tom Pister, the high school phys. ed. director, came to visit the sixth grades and we all met in the assembly and he was walking back and forth in front of the stage addressing us, talking about the importance of exercise and physical fitness and staying healthy, and Pister was what? Three hundred fifty? Four hundred pounds? More?

And you and I were on opposite ends of the same row and I leaned forward and looked down at you and you were looking back at me, both of us as if to say: so the bullshit starts now.

Well, fuck it. The Israelis are liars and takers; it's all they do, it's all they've ever done.

Hold that thought.

To: Andy Read
From: Rob Baltusrol
Subj: second thought

The whole idea of a Jewish homeland is bullshit. The idea that some 80-year-old Jew, living in Caracas (or Iran!) should go "home" to Israel…

He is home! He's been living there 80 years!!

To: karin@lotsalegs.com
From: Rob Baltusrol
Subj: Hey You

Is there anybody out there?

Wish you were here?

Shine on you crazy diamond?

Any of those do?

(Careful with that ax, Eugenie?)

To: Bill Torrey
From: Rob Baltusrol
Subj: re: Scouting Opportunities

Dear Mr. Torrey;

Which resume did I send?

Only kidding. Thank you very much for your reply. You have always been so kind to respond to my emails, whether they be the rants of an angry fan or something more sober. It is a touch of professionalism and class the Islanders have been woefully lacking since your departure (along with the Stanley Cups).

Best wishes,

Rob Baltusrol

On 6 May 2007, at 10:33, bill torrey <floridapanthershockey.com> wrote:

Hello Rob;

Of course I remember you. You were quite right about Oli Jokinen, and I've repeated many times your advice about only drafting players with the letter 'k' in their name, unless the letters are ORR.

Unfortunately our staff is full at present, and we really don't hire scouts unless they have years of junior hockey experience, which I gather from your resume you lack. But it was good to hear from you again, and I wish you all the best.

Bill Torrey
President, Florida Panthers

To: Mike Powers/WoodstockTV
From: Rob Baltusrol
Subj: re: last night

Free speech?

Or you could always tell them what I told them: the Israelis are liars and takers; it's all they do, it's all they've ever done.

Your choice.

On 7 May 2007, at 9:31, Mike Powers <woodstockpublictv.org> wrote:

As long as you feel good about yourself, Rob. That's the important thing.

And what do I tell the Albany Times? And the Herald-Record? Any thoughts on that?

On 7 May 2007, at 9:02, rob baltusrol wrote:

What about?

Mike: when I interviewed for this job, we all agreed: the purpose of public access TV was to air thoughts and opinions not expressed on mainstream, broadcast TV. And I think we can all agree that no thought is less expressed than Israel being the problem. Or, as ever, even on public access TV, is Israel the exception? (Talk about exceptionalism!)

I also said at the interview that if hired I would do everything I could to make Woodstock's public access television station the finest in the country. Didn't say I could do it, but said I would try. Mike: that's what I'm doing. As far as I'm concerned, I'm doing my job.

(And think of the ratings! We could be up to two dozen people by the end of the week!)

On 7 May 2007, at 8:50, Mike Powers <woodstockpublictv.org> wrote:

let's talk.

To: Andy Read
From: Rob Baltusrol
Subj: run away! run away!

By the way, A: Do you know what the plan was when I first got this job?

It was to link ALL cable public access stations in the country, have a show on nationally at seven o'clock in which we form a third party, we run our own elections, have our own debates, the people decide on a third party candidate to vote for then come election day we write that candidate in and start throwing all these bastard slime balls out. (Didn't exactly tell them that at the interview, of course.)

But, plans change.

To: karin@lotsalegs.com
From: Rob Baltusrol
Subj: re: hey you

Oh by way -- how's the pink???

On 7 May 2007, at 11:02, rob baltusrol wrote:

Is there anybody out there?

Wish you were here?

Shine on you crazy diamond?

Any of those do?

(Careful with that ax, Eugenie?)

To: Mike Powers/WoodstockTV
From: Rob Baltusrol
Subj: re: last night

The horse is out of the barn, Mike. Full gallop.

On 7 May 2007, at 9:48, Mike Powers <woodstockpublictv.org>
wrote:

Please tell me you're kidding.

On 7 May 2007, at 9:42, rob baltusrol wrote:

Free speech?

Or you could always tell them what I told them: the Israelis are liars and
takers; it's all they do, it's all they've ever done.

Your choice.

On 7 May 2007, at 9:31, Mike Powers <woodstockpublictv.org>
wrote:

As long as you feel good about yourself, Rob. That's the important
thing.

And what do I tell the Albany Times? And the Herald-Record? Any
thoughts on that?

On 7 May 2007, at 9:02, rob baltusrol wrote:

What about?

Mike: when I interviewed for this job, we all agreed: the purpose of public
access TV was to air thoughts and opinions not expressed on mainstream,
broadcast TV. And I think we can all agree that no thought is less
expressed than Israel being the problem. Or, as ever, even on public access
TV, is Israel the exception? (Talk about exceptionalism!)

From: Charles Wilcon
To: Rob Baltusrol
Subj: re: union

She was.

On 6 May 2007, at 13:02, rob baltusrol wrote:

It sure was. And I remember you telling me that story. (Another lifetime indeed.)

But enough about Richard, enough about Chich:

Chas: Chas: was she?

On 6 May 2007, at 12:11, charles wilcon wrote:

Yes there was. In the hills, of course. Some miles back, a major boozeup. Everyone it seemed, but you. Told stories though. Your first day, do you remember? Walking up on that ridge, that hat you used to wear, all alone. We were all looking at you, very cinemalike, and Richard~ remember Richard? Always wore the sink stopper in his vest? Looked like a watch chain? He turned and said, something tells me this is going to be a very interesting year.

Then Chich~ remember Mark Chichester? (More beer nuts!) He told of the time we were all at the rugger game and you had to go to the other side of the pitch to talk to your housemaster about something so you started walking the entire length of the field, Chich and I turned to watch you and as we did saw everyone else watching the game turn to watch you too! We both roared!

Some year, wasn't it?

From: karin@lotsalegs.com
To: Rob Baltusrol
Subj: re: hey you

I hope this isn't about fucking the Jews, rob.

Is it?

On 7 May 2007, at 12:22, rob baltusrol wrote:

Oh by the way -- how's the pink???

On 7 May 2007, at 11:02, rob baltusrol wrote:

Is there anybody out there?

Wish you were here?

Shine on you crazy diamond?

Any of those do?

(Careful with that ax, Eugenie?)

To: karin@lotsalegs.com
From: Rob Baltusrol
Subj: re: hey you

Just one. (The catch: repeatedly.)

On 7 May 2007, at 15:09, karin@lotsalegs.com wrote:

I hope this isn't about fucking the Jews, rob.

Is it?

On 7 May 2007, at 12:22, rob baltusrol wrote:

Oh by the way -- how's the pink???

On 7 May 2007, at 11:02, rob baltusrol wrote:

Is there anybody out there?

Wish you were here?

Shine on you crazy diamond?

Any of those do?

(Careful with that ax, Eugenie?)

To: Charles Wilcon
From: Rob Baltusrol
Subj: re: union

Chas, Chas: single? Still beautiful? What? Lonely? In love? *She misses me?!?!*

(Don't you dare walk away from your computer!)

On 7 May 2007, at 15:29, charles wilcon wrote:

She was.

On 6 May 2007, at 13:02, rob baltusrol wrote:

It sure was. And I remember you telling me that story. (Another lifetime indeed.)

But enough about Richard, enough about Chich:

Chas: Chas: was she?

On 6 May 2007, at 12:11, charles wilcon wrote:

Yes there was. In the hills, of course. Some miles back, a major boozeup. Everyone it seemed, but you. Told stories though. Your first day, do you remember? Walking up on that ridge, that hat you used to wear, all alone. We were all looking at you, very cinemalike, and Richard~ remember Richard? Always wore the sink stopper in his vest? Looked like a watch chain? He turned and said, something tells me this is going to be a very interesting year.

Then Chich~ remember Mark Chichester? (More beer nuts!) He told of the time we were all at the rugger game and you had to go to the other side of the pitch to talk to your housemaster about something so you started walking the entire length of the field, Chich and I turned to watch you and as we did saw everyone else watching the game turn to watch you too! We both roared!

Some year, wasn't it?

To: Margaret Hamilton
From: Rob Baltusrol
Subj: night editor position

Dear Peg;

Yada, yada, yada.

I would be happy to meet with you at your earliest convenience.

Sincerely,

Rob Baltusrol

To: Charles Wilcon
From: Rob Baltusrol
Subj: re:

My mother once said something interesting about Malvern, one of those comments, I took at the time, she got lucky with. (All parents do it.) But this time she was right. She said I never came back from Malvern, and I never did. And it's all tied to Bindy.

From: Claire Tansil
To: Rob Baltusrol
Subj: re:

I find it hard to believe, all these jobs you've had, been fired from, that you couldn't have kept. How come everyone else can keep a job, but not you? You think you're the only one with principles? Keeping a job is the principle. So is making a living.

I should have asked to read your play. You're right. But your not interested in my life, why should I be interested in yours?

And dioramas?? Very cute. Try a life! A life I've worked hard for and obtained, haven't sat around waiting for Mom to bail me out, or blaming everything on Dad and his mess. He didn't give me anything either.

On 6 May 2007, at 10:02, rob baltusrol wrote:

I've had jobs, Claire. Real jobs. Elevators and everything. I keep losing them. Why? Because the least welcome person in any newsroom in America is the best newsman in the place. That you find such a thought inconceivable is the problem -- so does most of America. They think journalism means Watergate. It means Lotto. It means someone I've never heard of is getting a divorce.

There's no winning with you, Claire. None. I tell you I win a playwriting contest and you don't ask to read the play. (A one-act!!) (Such reviews!) (Your brother the actor! Another direction! Another career!) I ask you to fill out a questionnaire for a side project of mine, shooting family documentaries, so I can get a better idea of which questions work best -- do you send it back? Do you fill it out? Of course not. (*Have* you ever shoplifted, Claire? I'm guessing not.)

You just pretend I don't do these things because it fits in much better with the picture of your brother the bum. You're perfect little world, no other world exists, and I'm not in it. Your little diorama. Doesn't matter what I do. No room. That's where the fireplace goes.

On 5 May 2007, at 16:44, Claire tansil wrote:

Swastikas, Rob? You're scaring me. What's next? Revolution? Storming the gates? You're becoming the type we read about, that bomber in the shack, shitting in the woods. Is that how you see yourself?

From: Charles Wilcon
To: Rob Baltusrol
Subj: story

What was the story you wanted to tell me? I wouldn't believe??

On 6 May 2007, at 13:02, rob baltusrol wrote:

It sure was. And I remember you telling me that story. (Another lifetime indeed.)

But enough about Richard, enough about Chich:

Chas: Chas: was she?

On 6 May 2007, at 12:11, charles wilcon wrote:

Yes there was. In the hills, of course. Some miles back, a major boozeup. Everyone it seemed, but you. Told stories though. Your first day, do you remember? Walking up on that ridge, that hat you used to wear, all alone. We were all looking at you, very cinemalike, and Richard~ remember Richard? Always wore the sink stopper in his vest? Looked like a watch chain? He turned and said, something tells me this is going to be a very interesting year.

Then Chich~ remember Mark Chichester? (More beer nuts!) He told of the time we were all at the rugger game and you had to go to the other side of the pitch to talk to your housemaster about something so you started walking the entire length of the field, Chich and I turned to watch you and as we did saw everyone else watching the game turn to watch you too! We both roared!

Some year, wasn't it?

To: Charles Wilcon
From: Rob Baltusrol
Subj: about which action taken in your life …

Unbelievable. Amsterdam. A few years back. I'm sitting in this coffee shop, yes one of those coffee shops, pleasantly stoned — do you know, every one of those places I went, and I went to several, everyone smoking wasn't drinking, and everyone drinking wasn't smoking? — anyway: sitting there, as I said. Still stoned. And who should walk in … but … Bindy. No, not Bindy today, Bindy yesterday. Bindy thirty years ago. I kid you not Chas, it was her. Exactly! Only one of two things: total fluke, or, most likely, it was her daughter. Had to be.

So I'm sitting there staring, obviously — she's as beautiful as ever — trying to get the nerve to get up and walk over … But… I couldn't. I froze. Paralyzed. And it wasn't the pot, Chas, it was much worse, it was shyness. (In a foreign land!) I simply could not get up. (And I had one of the great lines: "Excuse me, please: I know this sounds weird, but what's your mother's name?") Then twenty minutes later she does move, I watch her as she gets up, puts on her coat, turns and walks out the door back to the cold, cold canals. (It was freezing.)

A hand-delivered moment and I blew it!! Deprived myself of her looking up at me, with those gorgeous big beautiful eyes, and saying, "Me mum? Why, it's Bindy, why?"

Chas!! Chas!! Chas!!

(She could have been out buying pot for her mother!!)

But it taught me a great lesson, somehow. It taught me the opposite is also true: from nothing we can do something. Any of us can.

From: karin@lotsalegs.com
To: Rob Baltusrol
Subj: re: hey you

but it's what you're doing, isn't it? in some way. just think about it for
a moment. your a complicated guy, i've never heard anyone so
openly criticize Jews and israel. maybe it's what you get off on. well
maybe you get off on fucking this jew too. just think about it. (hey:
maybe I'm right!)

On 7 May 2007, at 16:02, rob baltusrol wrote:

Just one. (The catch: repeatedly.)

On 7 May 2007, at 15:09, karin@lotsalegs.com wrote:

I hope this isn't about fucking the Jews, rob.

Is it?

On 7 May 2007, at 12:22, rob baltusrol wrote:

Oh by the way -- how's the pink???

On 7 May 2007, at 11:02, rob baltusrol wrote:

Is there anybody out there?

Wish you were here?

Shine on you crazy diamond?

Any of those do?

(Careful with that ax, Eugenie?)

To: Charles Wilcon
From: Rob Baltusrol
Subj:

By the way, night wasn't a total loss. I went to some restaurant sat at the bar and a beautiful woman took the seat to my right. (Think Thandie Newton.) Never hit it off so quickly with a woman. She said early on her boyfriend was in bed with the flu. I said later let's give him a call, maybe he's taken a turn for the worse. She laughed, then it's the moment when she knows, and you know… and it's the most beautiful moment in the world.

(Why is it, no matter if you stay two weeks in a place or two days, the person you are intended to meet you meet your last night there?)

To: karin@lotsalegs.com
From: Rob Baltusrol
Subj:

Karin;

You are making the same mistake everyone does. (You!) I am not a complicated guy. I am simple as they come. I am the simplest guy in the world. Food, clothing, shelter, that's it for me. (But for everyone.)

To: karin@lotsalegs.com
From: Rob Baltusrol
Subj: come again

And let me be more blunt. You beautiful fucking Jew. This is one of the best relationships I have ever been in. Yes, all we do is fuck. That's why it's one of the best relationships I've ever been in. I love fucking you. The only thing I like more than fucking you is fucking you again. I look at you and get hard. And, judging by the fact by the time I walk over and push my hand down your pants you're wet too, I'm guessing you feel the same way. This is what you and I were meant to do, we met and we're doing it.

Got news for you, Dollface: this is as close to love as it gets.

From: Claire Tansil
To: Rob Baltusrol
Subj:

And three cars from Mom. That's pathetic.

From: Bryan Milbury
To: Rob Baltusrol
Subj: re: three for three

Do you really expect to find work this way?
bm

On 7 May 2007, at 16:06, rob baltusrol wrote:

Portrait of Dorien Grey?

Actually, it's The Picture of Dorian Gray.

(And they're Labradors, not Labor dogs.)

On 9 April 2007, at 15:50, bryan milbury<newsday.com> wrote:

Dear Mr. Baltursol;

Re: your letter of May 29 offering your copy editing services:
thank you but we are quite satisfied with the staff we have
already. And think your cause would be far better served by
the sending out of a more professional letter.

Rgds.

Bryan Milbury
Mng. Ed.

From: karin@lotsalegs.com
To: Rob Baltusrol
Subj: re:

crystal. [sigh]

On 6 May 2007, at 22:32, rob baltusrol wrote:

I can't wait to fuck you. I can't wait for you to walk through the door and drop to your knees and take my cock into that luscious mouth then stand you up and turn you around and lean you over the counter and repeatedly fuck that perfect pussy, that perfect ass.

Now: is it clear what awaits in Hurley?

To: Allison Hirst
From: Rob Baltusrol
Subj: re:

Allison;

Thanks for that link, had not read it.

You ask me, 9/11, more than the most spectacular criminal attack of all time, it's the most contaminated crime scene of all time. Picture a guy in an English country manor making his way through the drawing room, stepping over the corpse, and dropping ... a dead fish ... a page from a 20-year-old calendar ... an Enya cd ... a candlestick? ... some ivory cufflinks for good measure.

Now: try and solve the crime, what the real clues are. That's what 9/11 is for me. We've just got to separate the clues from the cufflinks and the candlestick. (And by all means, from the Enya cd.)

(The web fairy ... love it.) (The Plane and the Pentagon ... sounds like a fairy tale to me.)

On 7 May 2007, at 21:51, twoginsshaken@bellsouth.net wrote:

Hi Rob;

I know you're up on the whole 9/11 stuff, thought this might interest you. Jury's still out for me, I guess I'm just not the cynic you are. (Keep trying!)
Allison

http://www.thewebfairy.com/911/93/mayor/htm

To: Claire Tansil
From: Rob Baltusrol
Subj:

Didn't give you anything? Dad? Are you serious?

He gave you everything, Claire, the only thing, a sense of purpose. And I can tell you exactly when he gave it to you -- it was the day you returned to public school after two years at Buckley (oh, the horror!) and then and there, from that moment on, everything you've done from the Creek Club wedding to the board of directors at Piping Rock was cast in stone. All of it. Never gave you anything?

What's he given me?

From: Sebastian Baltusrol
To: Rob Baltusrol
Subj: re: going once ... going twice ...

well, remember how you told me you thought taking spanish might be a
good idea. for when I was living in Spain. I know you were kidding,
actually, you weren't I don't think, well..

long story, short, dad, mila, my spanish teacher's daughter. I think I
mentioned her. I know I did, I wrote to a very long email once, I
mentioned her once and the only thing you emailed me back was, "mila"?
remember? yeah. that mila.

well things got very serious between us and there both going back this
summer, to spain, and yes I want to go with them. I love her very much,
and she loves me, and if it doesn't work out it doesn't but what if it does?
that's what I'm thinking, dad. and you always said, above everything else,
to think for myself. well, that's what I'm doing. (its all your fault!)

give it a few days before you tell me what you htink okay? It's good dad.
really. I wake up with a smile on my face. (i like going to school!!!!)

sebastian

you'd love her dad. (and you get to visit us in spain.)

On 6 May 2007, at 9:52, rob baltusrol wrote:

Sebastian:

I'm not in the mood: what about college?

On 5 May 2007, at 13:11, sebastian baltusrol wrote:

hi dad

sorry it's been awhile, busy busy. But, uh, about college..

--the $400 was a joke, right?--

On 2 May 2007, at 9:52, rob baltusrol wrote:

To: Sebastian Baltusrol
From: Rob Baltusrol
Subj: rain on the plain

Sebastian: your English and grammar aside (is your Spanish any better?) (Surprise me once; capitalize SOMETHING) …

I get it, Sebastian, first love. Nothing like it. Something you will only fully appreciate some 30 years from now: BUT:

What do you intend to do in Spain? Seriously. Besides being in love. Have you given it any thought? How would you reside there? Legally? Are you planning on marrying? Does her father own a business? (Is there free olive oil in this deal?)

Seriously, Sebastian: What would you do? Not today, but tomorrow. Have you thought about that? I know you'll be 18 soon, all these decisions will be yours, but sometimes you have problems with the questions, Sebastian. You don't ask them. And this just seems so rash and rash decisions, almost always, the worst.

(Yes, Sebastian, I am asking you to consider YOUR FUTURE.)

To: Claire Tansil
From: Rob Baltusrol
Subj: ouch

Claire;

I'm not going to waste time with this anymore. You have your life, I have mine, occasionally they meet and explode.

But you do make one good point. The cars. Believe it or not, until you pointed that out, it really never occurred to me that she gave me three cars, and you're right. That is pathetic. (The first Taurus, I did pay some, I think about $1200.)

On 7 May 2007, at 16:02, claire tansil wrote:

And three cars from Mom? That's pathetic.

To: Morton Library
From: Rob Baltusrol
Subj: invasion of the singing snatchers

Charlis;

Yes, I know it's Meryl Streep, and yes, I know it's Greece, and yes, I know it's ABBA, but do not — repeat DO NOT — rent "Mama Mia!" You'll thank me.

To: Andy Read
From: Rob Baltusrol
Subj: the waiting is the hardest part

Tomorrow's the day, pal, if the Albany Times, etc., quote me accurately, or if the editor dares run it. After that it's only a question of whether Foxman bites ...

tick ... tick ... tick ...

To: Claire Tansil
From: Rob Baltusrol
Subj: re:

And it may surprise you, Claire, but nothing matters more to me than getting the respect of my family, nothing bothers me more than not getting it.

On 7 May 2007, at 16:02, claire tansil wrote:

And three cars from Mom? That's pathetic.

From: Charles Wilcon
To: Rob Baltusrol
Subj: re: Boy the way Glenn Miller played ...

Bloody hell! Now I know why she means so much to you.

On 6 May 2007, at 23:59, rob baltusrol wrote:

I can't believe I never told you this. Yeah. She came down at least a dozen times. (Exactly a dozen times, as a matter of fact. I counted.)

I'd wait up 'til about 2 or so — it's amazing, considering how much time I was awake, how little homework I did — then creep through the house, through the grounds and up to Ellerslie to fetch her. (Remember, Chas, this was at a time when food wasn't allowed in your room.) We'd come back down, walk through the kitchen, up flights of stairs, tip-toeing past some 30 odd sleeping kids, not one of which ever waked and if one ever did ... doom. Unbelievable.

Wait. I haven't even told you the good part. I had a private room, remember. Everyone else had a cubicle, except to get to my room I had to walk through another room with four beds where four 12-year-olds, I think they were, slept. The first night Bindy came down, leaving early in the morning: they're awake! So I introduced them! Then I walk Bindy out, quickly go back up and there they are sitting up in bed. Smiling. So I said, "Guys. I know what it's like to have a secret, especially one when your twelve years old, but you can not tell anyone this. And I need you to promise that you won't -- because it might happen again!" (Shades of Canterbury Tales, right?) And they promised, and they never did. And Bindy and I carried on the whole time as if we knew they wouldn't.

Chas: I can't even believe I'm telling you this, yet I lived it and didn't think a thing!

112

From: Claire Tansil
To: Rob Baltusrol
Subj: re:

I don't respect you. Nobody does.

On 8 May 2007, at 23:06, rob baltusrol wrote:

And it may surprise you, Claire, but nothing matters more to me than getting the respect of my family, nothing bothers me more than not getting it.

On 7 May 2007, at 16:02, claire tansil wrote:

And three cars from Mom? That's pathetic.

To: Andy Read
From: Rob Baltusrol
Subj: ... tock.

He bit.

To: Mike Powers/WoodstockTV
From: Rob Baltustrol
Subj: re: O'Reilly show

Titles only on TV, Mike.

Besides: Woodstock has the name recognition of Gandhi. It's time we started doing something with it.

We changed the world once. Why not change it again? (Harder! Harder!)

On 9 May 2007, at 9:52, Mike Powers <woodstockpublictv.org> wrote:

just heard you were going on O'Reilly show. trust you're going as private citizen?

From: karin@lotsalegs.com
To: Rob Baltusrol
Subj: re: come again

and yes it's fucking, no question about it. fuck me all the time wonderful fucking. but it's when we're fucking, when you're fucking me, and I'm fucking you, that I realize how much I love you. and that's never happened before.

On 7 May 2007, at 15:48, rob baltusrol wrote:

And let me be more blunt. You beautiful fucking Jew. This is one of the best relationships I have ever been in. Yes, all we do is fuck. That's why it's one of the best relationships I've ever been in. I love fucking you. The only thing I like more than fucking you is fucking you again. I look at you and get hard. And, judging by the fact by the time I walk over and push my hand down your pants you're wet too, I'm guessing you feel the same way. This is what you and I were meant to do, we met and we're doing it.

Got news for you, Dollface: this is as close to love as it gets.

To: karin@lotsalegs.com
From: Rob Baltusrol
Subj: re: come again

Now that's what I call an email exchange!

On 9 May 2007, at 11:44, karin@lotsalegs.com wrote:

and yes it's fucking, no question about it. fuck me all the time wonderful fucking. but it's when we're fucking, when you're fucking me, and I'm fucking you, that I realize how much I love you. and that's never happened before.

On 7 May 2007, at 15:48, rob baltusrol wrote:

And let me be more blunt. You beautiful fucking Jew. This is one of the best relationships I have ever been in. Yes, all we do is fuck. That's why it's one of the best relationships I've ever been in. I love fucking you. The only thing I like more than fucking you is fucking you again. I look at you and get hard. And, judging by the fact by the time I walk over and push my hand down your pants you're wet too, I'm guessing you feel the same way. This is what you and I were meant to do, we met and we're doing it.

Got news for you, Dollface: this is as close to love as it gets.

From: Sebastian Baltusrol
To: Rob Baltusrol
Subj: kettle pot

rash, dad? what job was it you had once, a newspaper I think, you hated so bad you looked out the window one day and saw the landscaping crew and got up from your chair and went downstairs and asked them for a job. an hour later you were riding a mower and waving up at your editor through the window? didn't you tell me something like that once?

and I am thinking about tomorrow. tommorrow is exactly what I'm thinking about..

On 7 May 2007, at 11:32, rob baltusrol wrote:

Sebastian: your English and grammar aside (is your Spanish any better?) (Surprise me once; capitalize SOMETHING) …

I get it, Sebastian, first love. Nothing like it. Something you will only fully appreciate some 30 years from now: BUT:

What do you intend to do in Spain? Seriously. Besides being in love. Have you given it any thought? How would you reside there? Legally? Are you planning on marrying? Does her father own a business? (Is there free olive oil in this deal?)

Seriously, Sebastian: What would you do? Not today, but tomorrow. Have you thought about that? I know you'll be 18 soon, all these decisions will be yours, but sometimes you have problems with the questions, Sebastian. You don't ask them. And this just seems so rash and rash decisions, almost always, the worst.

(Yes, Sebastian, I am asking you to consider YOUR FUTURE.)

From: Andy Read
To: Rob Baltusrol
Subj: re: he rang

O'Reilly? I thought you said Larry King. Boo!! (Kidding, of course.)

On 9 May 2007, at 8:59, rob baltusrol wrote:

Got the call. O'Reilly. Tonight.

From: The Saugerties Times
To: Rob Baltusrol
Subj: re: Yard Sale

Don't get it. Sorry.
EF

On 19 April 2007, at 11:39, rob baltusrol wrote:

Editor;

I submit the following for any section of your paper. Thank you.

Rob Baltusrol

YARD SALE NOTICE!
Numerous readers have asked us to once again print public statute 13a
subsection iv regarding suitable use of the term "yard sale," which
according to the statute does not mean throwing things at the end of your
yard "willy-nilly" but must be meant to include certain inalienable items
to be properly — *and legally* — considered a yard sale.
The statute was written in 1977 in response to a simultaneous, nationwide
unloading of two million copies of Debby Boone's *You Light Up My Life*,
and yard sale experts to this day consider it one of the most unusual laws
of its kind.
Yard sales, which under the statute qualify as a "hand-drawn sign"
business, must offer at least five of the following items for sale to be
"fairly and decently" considered a yard sale. To wit:
A six-color globe, minimum 14 inches diameter. (Illuminated globes count
as two items.) Skis, and any two bindings, boots, or poles. (A wooden
toboggan of any size may be substituted, or two sleds of no considerable
rust);
A croquet set containing a minimum four balls from the original set, three
usable mallets *from any set* [original italics], and six wickets. A badminton
set may be substituted Memorial through Labor Day provided three
working rackets and two birdies exist;
Books, a third of which must be hardback, no more than a quarter of those
book club editions, and no more than half missing dust jackets. Fifty
percent of books may be price-clipped, not including first editions whose
total number of sales exceeded by more than ten times the number in the
original run; Games; must contain all original pieces, 'Mousetrap' and
'Operation' included.
And final warning: selling used artificial Christmas trees is a class 4
misdemeanor. (For selling unused artificial Christmas trees — still in box
— see subsection vii, paragraph 4: "The Beatles Flip-Your-Wig game and
other novelty items.")

From: Sebastian Baltusrol
To: Rob Baltusrol
Subj: re: rain on the plain

and my future......says the 50 yr old station manger for the public access
television station in the booming metropolis of Woodstock NY pulling
down--20 gs a year?

--sorry. couldn't resist--

On 7 May 2007, at 11:32, rob baltusrol wrote:

Sebastian: your English and grammar aside (is your Spanish any better?)
(Surprise me once; capitalize SOMETHING) ...

I get it, Sebastian, first love. Nothing like it. Something you will only fully
appreciate some 30 years from now: BUT:

What do you intend to do in Spain? Seriously. Besides being in love. Have
you given it any thought? How would you reside there? Legally? Are you
planning on marrying? Does her father own a business? (Is there free olive
oil in this deal?)

Seriously, Sebastian: What would you do? Not today, but tomorrow. Have
you thought about that? I know you'll be 18 soon, all these decisions will
be yours, but sometimes you have problems with the questions, Sebastian.
You don't ask them. And this just seems so rash and rash decisions, almost
always, the worst.

(Yes, Sebastian, I am asking you to consider YOUR FUTURE.)

To: Sebastian Baltusrol
From: Rob Baltusrol
Subj: re: rain on the plain

Program director.

25.

Wiseass.

(And I might be wrong, but I think a manger is that thing … oh forget it.)

On 9 May 2007, at 19:02, sebastian baltusrol wrote:

and my future……says the 50 yr old station manger for the public access
television station in the booming metropolis of Woodstock NY pulling
down--20 gs a year?

--sorry. couldn't resist--

On 7 May 2007, at 11:32, rob baltusrol wrote:

Sebastian: your English and grammar aside (is your Spanish any better?)
(Surprise me once; capitalize SOMETHING) …

I get it, Sebastian, first love. Nothing like it. Something you will only fully
appreciate some 30 years from now: BUT:

What do you intend to do in Spain? Seriously. Besides being in love. Have
you given it any thought? How would you reside there? Legally? Are you
planning on marrying? Does her father own a business? (Is there free olive
oil in this deal?)

Seriously, Sebastian: What would you do? Not today, but tomorrow. Have
you thought about that? I know you'll be 18 soon, all these decisions will
be yours, but sometimes you have problems with the questions, Sebastian.
You don't ask them. And this just seems so rash and rash decisions, almost
always, the worst.

(Yes, Sebastian, I am asking you to consider YOUR FUTURE.)

To: Andy Read
From: Rob Baltusrol
Subj: re: ... tock.

No. It was always O'Reilly. That's why I included the line about Jewish culpability in the greatest crime in American history, the murder of Santa Claus. Knew that was O'Reilly's thing and he couldn't resist. (Yoo-hoo! Over here!)

Catnip.

On 9 May 2007, at 9:21, andy read wrote:

O'Reilly? I thought you said Larry King. Boo!! (Kidding, of course.)

On 9 May 2007, at 8:59, rob baltusrol wrote:

Got the call. O'Reilly. Tonight.

To: Andy Read
From: Rob Baltusrol
Subj: hannukah bush anyone?

Speaking of which: saw the other day some film where some woman was making a bar mitzvah cake with an American flag on top! (Greer Garson would never have stooped so low.) Then caught an interview Diane Sawyer did with Ahmadinejad and you'd swear the translator attended the Mel Blanc school of Arab translation.

Can only assume snake wrestler on the nature channel was wearing a Brandeis T-shirt.

On 9 May 2007, at 9:21, andy read wrote:

O'Reilly? I thought you said Larry King. Boo!! (Kidding, of course.)

On 9 May 2007, at 8:59, rob baltusrol wrote:

Got the call. O'Reilly. Tonight.

From: karin@lotsaleggins
To: Rob Baltusrol
Subj: re: shit meets fan

no, I did not catch that. that's wonderful. thanks for pointing that out. (seen here taken into custody for repeated fornication with with, with who?

what's the penalty for repeated fornication with you, anyway?

On 9 May 2007, at 15:29, rob baltusrol wrote:

They're always going to use the worst picture. Back during the cold war, every picture you saw of Moscow it was cloudy. Then perestroika came and all of a sudden the sun came out.

You notice how close your hands were together? Made you look like you were wearing handcuffs.

On 9 May 2007, at 15:11, karin@lotsalegs.com wrote:

doesn't get any worse (til dad sees it)

and you should see the picture they used. made me look like a criminal.

On 9 May 2007, at 14:37, rob baltusrol wrote:

How bad?

On 9 May 2007, at 14:06, karin@lotsalegs.com wrote:

mom just saw a picture of us. shit shit shit

To: karin@lotsalegs.com
From: Rob Baltusrol
Subj: re: shit meets fan

Life.

On 9 May 2007, at 15:44, karin@lotsalegs.com wrote:

no, I did not catch that. wonderful. thanks for pointing that out.
(seen here taken into custody for repeated fornication with with,
with who?

What's the penalty for repeated fornication with you, anyway?

On 9 May 2007, at 15:29, rob baltusrol wrote:

They're always going to use the worst picture. Back during the cold war,
every picture you saw of Moscow it was cloudy. Then perestroika came
and all of a sudden the sun came out.

You notice how close your hands were together? Made you look like you
were wearing handcuffs.

On 9 May 2007, at 15:11, karin@lotsalegs.com wrote:

doesn't get any worse (til dad sees it)

and you should see the picture they used. made me look like a
criminal.

On 9 May 2007, at 14:37, rob baltusrol wrote:

How bad?

On 9 May 2007, at 14:06, karin@lotsalegs.com wrote:

mom just saw a picture of us. shit shit shit

From: Jim Natalini
To: Rob Baltusrol
Subj: re: I should have known better

I dropped by, Rob. I had your money. I wasn't about to leave that much cash under the mat. I get paid again next Thursday. I'll get it to you then, maybe not all but close. And I don't know what ladder your talking about.

On 29 April 2007, at 14:54, rob baltusrol wrote:

Jim;

I have a theory that people who use the word "Kafkaesque" are least likely to have ever read a word of Kafka. Similarly those whose shelves are stocked with books on yoga and meditation are the ones most likely to be short on the rent, and to forget to return your ladder. And they more than anyone better pray to God (whichever one they pray to) that what goes around doesn't come around.

They could also put down the Bagdavita every once in awhile and pick up Emily Post.

Rob

Draft Folder
subj: journal

All the bullshit, all the fuckups, all the failures; all the assholes, all the asswipe jobs; the shitty cars, the clueless, gutless hack bosses, the backstabbers, the disrespect; the women whose emails stopped coming, the friends who left, the lonely pathetic solitary existence.

That all ends tonight.

Just be yourself.

Within reason.

To: karin@lotsalegs.com
From: Rob Baltusrol
Subj:

Karin, fuck it: I do love you.

To: Andy Read
From: Rob Baltusrol
Subj: re:

You like the sweater? Couldn't you just hear that old Old Spice music in the background? The guy returning from the sea?

Shen was a journalism teacher I had at BU and was guessing O'Reilly had him too. (Everyone did.) You see his face when I mentioned his name? Looked like the guy in the Godfather about to testify then looks out at the crowd and sees his brother, flown in from Italy. That would be Shen. ("Yeah! The family had a lot of buffers!")

(And ALWAYS start with a joke.)

On 9 May 2007, at 22:05, andy read wrote:

Fucking brilliant, pal. Perfectly pitched performance. Every note. Perfect. Bravo!

(Who's James Shen?)

To: Andy Read
From: Rob Baltusrol
Subj: job #33424

Reminds me: I used to work with this guy — two-day job — sold frozen meat and fish door-to-door. Give homeowners some line about supplying local restaurants, there being an over-order. The trick, he said, incredible guy, was to get the product into the kitchen. And how he did that, soon as the homeowner asked a question he'd say, "Let me show you" and was walking by them with an armload of fish.

As soon as O'Reilly went quiet when I compared Nazism and Zionism, saying both were national movements based on racial purity, I was walking by him with an armload of fish.

On 9 May 2007, at 22:05, andy read wrote:

Fucking brilliant, pal. Perfectly pitched performance. Every note. Perfect. Bravo!

(Who's James Shen?)

From: Sebastian Baltusrol
To: Rob Baltusrol
Subj:

dad;

remember the time on the lake? I'm sure you do, it was a real windy day, you rented a sailboat and had never sailed before (never told me that) and you were sailing against the wind, I forget what it's called, and nobody on the lake was trying what you were trying, people with boats dad, people who KNEW HOW TO SAIL weren't doing it.

But we made it. I was yelling the whole time but you sailed straight into the marina and never used your engine and you docked and I remember how happy you were.

I know going to Spain is a big decision, I know it's not something a lot of people would do, or maybe anyone. But I think sometimes you forget who my father is.

(and I'm sorry I yelled, dad. I told mila that story and she said your father sounds great. You are great.)

To: Sebastian Baltusrol
From: Rob Baltusrol
Subj: re:

Thanks for that, Sebastian.

You had every right to yell. And I know I give you plenty of causes to, but worse is to give you none. You and I have never talked about my father, really, but I have no stories like that. Not one. Hard guy to want to yell at, even when he was drunk, which was most the time. He was there, but he floated. He left me alone, but I don't want to leave you alone, Sebastian, and I don't want to float. Only one per family, sorry.

On 10 May 2007, at 11:11, sebastian baltusrol wrote:

dad;

remember the time on the lake? I'm sure you do, it was a real windy day, you rented a sailboat and had never sailed before (never told me that) and you were sailing against the wind, I forget what it's called, and nobody on the lake was trying what you were trying, people with boats dad, people who KNEW HOW TO SAIL weren't doing it.

But we made it. I was yelling the whole time but you sailed straight into the marina and never used your engine and you docked and I remember how happy you were.

I know going to Spain is a big decision, I know it's not something a lot of people would do, or maybe anyone. But I think sometimes you forget who my father is.

(and I'm sorry I yelled, dad. I told mila that story and she said your father sounds great. You are great.)

From: Andy Read
To: Rob Baltusrol
Subj: re: Kim, Kim it's only a movie

He's a producer at Fox. He was just on one of their shows, said you two worked together in Savannah and you're the smartest guy he's ever known. Host asked him about 9/11, if he thought O'Reilly should do the show, and he kind of smiled and hemmed and hawed and said, if it was anybody else…

(Also said a school superintendent you were interviewing down there threw you out of his office!)

On 10 May 2007, at 11:58, rob baltusrol wrote:

Cantor… Yes. Refresh my memory.

On 10 May 2007, at 11:51, andy read wrote:

Ever heard of a guy named Mark Cantor?

On 8 May 2007, at 21:12, rob baltusrol wrote:

By the way, you see where this Obama guy is running for president? You see the cover of his book: the suit, no tie?

Who the fuck wears a suit without a tie? (For a *photo shoot?!?*)

(Hmmm… Casual Republican? Or serious Democrat?)

Just another fucking clown.

To: Karin@lotsalegs
From: Rob Baltusrol
Subj: re:

I can't help you here, Karin.

On 10 May, at 11:55, karin@lotsalegs.com wrote:

he saw it.

this is bad, Rob, real bad. I feel like I'm walking around with a great big T on my chest and it's not for tits, it's for traitor. i feel awful, awful awful

To: Andy Read
From: Rob Baltusrol
Subj: re: Kim, Kim it's only a movie

Good old Mark....

He's a hell of a producer, by the way. (Jewish. He once asked me to work
for him "next Monday." Said his folks were in town. Next Monday turned
out to be Labor Day. Brought in his folks to introduce them, said they'd be
watching that night. I lead with two pro-Palestinian pieces! Local news!!)

On 10 May 2007, at 12:02, andy read wrote:

He's a producer at Fox. He was just on one of their shows, said you two
worked together in Savannah and you're the smartest guy he's ever
known. Host asked him about 9/11, if he thought O'Reilly should do the
show, and he kind of smiled and hemmed and hawed and said, if it was
anybody else...

(Also said a school superintendent you were interviewing down there
threw you out of his office!)

On 10 May 2007, at 11:58, rob baltusrol wrote:

Cantor... Yes. Refresh my memory.

On 10 May 2007, at 11:51, andy read wrote:

Ever heard of a guy named Mark Cantor?

On 8 May 2007, at 21:12, rob baltusrol wrote:

By the way, you see where this Obama guy is running for president? You
see the cover of his book: the suit, no tie?

Who the fuck wears a suit without a tie? (For a *photo shoot?!?*)

136

From: karin@lotsalegs.com
To: Rob Baltusrol
Subj:

you know, I'm not asking for sympathy, Rob, i'm really not. i just
wish once in awhile you'd see it from my side. or just once. first,
you're not Jewish. so already my folks can't stand you. but wait,
dad, there's more. you know that guy who called Elie Wiesel the
biggest fraud on the face of the earth? you know: the same guy you
called the greatest enemy to the Jewish people since Hitler? your
daughter's fucking him.

To: Sebastian Baltusrol
From: Rob Baltusrol
Subj: re:

Wasn't all grim, Sebastian. Rallied for Christmas every year, those are the two things I'll remember from childhood, Creek Club (however briefly) and Christmas. It's more than a lot of people get.

On 10 May 2007, at 12:32, sebastian baltusrol wrote:

i did not know that dad.

On 10 May 2007, at 12:22, rob baltusrol wrote:

Thanks for that, Sebastian.

You had every right to yell. And I know I give you plenty of causes to, but worse is to give you none. You and I have never talked about my father, really, but I have no stories like that. Not one. Hard guy to want to yell at, even when he was drunk, which was most the time. He was there, but he floated. He left me alone, but I don't want to leave you alone, Sebastian, and I don't want to float. Only one per family, sorry.

On 10 May 2007, at 11:11, sebastian baltusrol wrote:

dad;

remember the time on the lake? I'm sure you do, it was a real windy day, you rented a sailboat and had never sailed before (never told me that) and you were sailing against the wind, I forget what it's called, and nobody on the lake was trying what you were trying, people with boats dad, people who KNEW HOW TO SAIL weren't doing it.

But we made it. I was yelling the whole time but you sailed straight into the marina and never used your engine and you docked and I remember how happy you were.

I know going to Spain is a big decision, I know it's not something a lot of people would do, or maybe anyone. But I think sometimes you forget who my father is.

To: Andy Read
From: Rob Baltusrol
Subj: don't look down

We're on!! Fox said yes!!

Steven Jones and Griffith have already confirmed, it will be the three of us.

(Never thought I'd see the day, but God bless Bill O'Reilly.) (And James Shen.) (And Mark Cantor!)

A lot of this will be done on the fly, but still we'll need a call to arms, some line. (Mad as hell and not going to … ? No.) I'll have to think of something.

Question is: *now* what sweater do I wear?

From: Karin@lotsalegs.com
To: Rob Baltusrol
Subj: re:

will you stop!!

On 10 May 2007, at 12:59, rob baltusrol wrote:

Elie Wiesel. The Jews' pope.

On 10 May 2007, at 12:52, karin@lotsalegs.com wrote:

you know, I'm not asking for sympathy, Rob, i'm really not. i just
wish once in awhile you'd see it from my side. or just once. first,
you're not Jewish. so already my folks can't stand you. but wait,
dad, there's more. you know that guy who called Elie Wiesel the
biggest fraud on the face of the earth? you know: the same guy you
called the greatest enemy to the Jewish people since Hitler? your
daughter's fucking him.

To: Andy Read
From: Rob Baltusrol
Subj: kingdom for a horse, was it?

And has it occurred to you that far more history is made by the Donna
Rices of the world than the Gary Harts?

To: Sebastian Baltusrol
From: Rob Baltusrol
Subj:

And by the way, Sebastian: I know you're going to think I'm kidding, but I'm not.

I fully believe in Santa Claus. No, not the concept. The person. The North Pole. I truly, fully, completely believe he's up there.

To: Karin@lotslegs.com
From: Rob Baltusrol
Subj: re:

And I still say the T is for tits!

On 10 May 2007, at 12:52, karin@lotsalegs.com wrote:

you know, I'm not asking for sympathy, Rob, i'm really not. i just
wish once in awhile you'd see it from my side. or just once. first,
you're not Jewish. so already my folks can't stand you. but wait,
dad, there's more. you know that guy who called Elie Wiesel the
biggest fraud on the face of the earth? you know: the same guy you
called the greatest enemy to the Jewish people since Hitler? your
daughter's fucking him.

To: Marcello Robertson
From: Rob Baltusrol
Subj: re: bad rice

Dear Marcello;

Thank you for your email, though obviously I would have liked its contents to be different.

I have another script, if you're interested. It's about an alcoholic whose decision to quit drinking turns out to be the worst decision of his life. And believe it or not, it's a comedy too.

I can send it if you like. Cheers.

Rob.

On 9 May 2007, at 10:40, marcello robertson
<robertsonentertainment.com> wrote:

```
Thank you for letting me read Bad Rice, but I
must say I didn't find the script to be funny at
all. In fact, I'm not sure I laughed once. But I
thank you for letting me read it and wish you all
the best.
Marcello
```

From: Andy Read
To: Rob Baltusrol
Subj: the show

Rob:

I went to Murphy's. Remember Murphy's? Where we used to watch the
Islander games? Pretty much same crowd. Which is to say, utterly
completely lethargic (which is how we used to get to watch Islander
games in Bruins country).

I was at the bar. People were playing pool, the jukebox was on, sounding
same as always, probably same songs. I waited until two minutes before 8,
just wanted to see if someone else would ask for O'Reilly show. Someone
did. Someone asked to turn the volume up. "This nut," someone said.
"Pretty sharp nut." Someone else said. Who? "The guy from last night,"
he said. "In the sweater." I'm NOT KIDDING. Said someone else: "9/11
guy last night." Someone else asked to turn down the jukebox, the
bartender, same bartender, she must be 80, Cathy? Who has never broken
a smile in her life. She turned the jukebox off! (In Murphy's!)

Soon, nobody was talking. No one ordered a thing. The bartender didn't
move. People from the pool room started walking in. No one was playing
pool for an hour, Rob. For an hour. In Murphy's!! People came in off the
street, looking through the windows, stopped dead in their tracks. People
who had never been in Murphy's in their lives. Everyone was standing
staring at the television set. There was complete silence.

And then when you said, "What would it take to end all wars? One phone
call. One phone call from everyone to these bastards in Washington. Well
we are at war: with them!"

And the bar exploded. People were standing and cheering, drunks who
hadn't lifted their heads in years were all standing and laughing, strangers
were hugging, Cathy was smiling. And I just sobbed. I just sobbed
thinking the whole time, I know that guy. Two weeks ago he told me all of
this.

To: Andy Read
From: Rob Baltusrol
Subj:

Murphy's!! Brilliant idea, pal. (If they can wake up at Murphy's...) (They still have My Shirona on the jukebox?)

I know I was grandstanding with the bit about one lousy phone call and I'll give you a show you won't believe, but that's what it's got to be, a show. Getting something for free, a pledge drive without the money, call not for me but for yourselves, or else it won't work.

You want a person's participation, that's the last thing you ask for. You ask them if they like cookies.

To: Rob Baltusrol
From: Riggs Plumbing Supply
Subj: re: bidets con't

When did you come in off the street?

On 6 May 2007, at 15:41, rob baltusrol wrote:

Mills;

Or, we could always go with straight humor.

How about this for bidets, big headline:

FIRST THINGS FIRST

Rob

On 4 May 2007, at 19:02, rob baltusrol wrote:

Hello Mills.

I walked in off the street the other day, asked you some questions about bidets, how many you sold, mentioned I did some advertising and would you be interested if I came up with any ideas. You said yes. Well, I think I have.

What do you think of this line:

Bidets. *A nice thing about civilization.*

I don't know if we'd use it on your website, or maybe we could run it in the local paper. But I do think bidets in this country are something people are ready to buy, just have to be nudged a little. Then it's, "Honey, call me crazy, but you know what I'm thinking of buying…?" (Maybe *there's* our line!)

To: Andy Read
From: Rob Baltusrol
Subj:

I ever tell you my pickup trick at Murphy's? I'd put Suffragette City on the jukebox, wait til the part, "Wham Bam Thank You Ma'am," see which girl was singing it the loudest, then walk over..

Ah …. what a fucking meat market that place was. (Remember Sweepstakes?)

To: karin@lotsalegs.com
From: Rob Baltusrol
Subj: no words

Karin;

Now you know why I hate the phone.

From: Cynthia Dwyer
To: Rob Baltusrol
Subj: Hi Rob! It's me!

Hi, Rob. It's Cynthia Dwyer. From high school. Remember me? I got you email address from Debbie Cekala from our 20th reunion. (Remember that? On the beach? Mr. Lambrech threw up??)

I just want you to know I got calls from all my family because I told them to watch. And they're all calling their congressmen and senators and the White house. (They all said, You know that guy? I said of course: he used to come to all my birthday parties!! My Mom said, that was that white kid?!? I said, "He's still that white kid!"

Do you remember what I wrote in your yearbook? I still mean it. I see I was right. (You wrote, stay in touch. So there!)

(And you're still the cutest!!)

Love to you,

Cynthia

From: City Lights Theatre
To: Rob Baltusrol
Subj: Now He's Perking for Sasha

Hello Rob

We have taken a second look at your play and agree it's something we'd like to do.
Would you still want to direct?

All the best,
Jim Chapin
City Lights Theatre

From: karin@lotsalegs.com
To: Rob Baltusrol
Subj: re: no words

rob, I can't even speak right now, Im so upset. I cried all night. you are so amazing, you have given me so much and I thank you for everything.

when I think, if we hadn't met in that parking lot...

On 11 May 2007, at 10:17, rob baltusrol wrote:

Karin;

Now you know why I hate the phone.

To: Key West Water Sports
From: Rob Baltusrol
Subj: holy chutzpah

Mike:

Are you out of your fucking mind?

You rip me off $800 and want to friend me on facebook??

How much you rip off your other friends for?

To: karin@lotsalegs
From: Rob Baltusrol
Subj: re: no words

Er…. Can I come clean?

We didn't just meet. I saw you on line and I wanted you. Why do you think I slowed down, started going over my receipt? (Actually, I was seeing how much she charged me for the apples.)

I wanted you to catch up. I wanted to walk together. Do you know how much can change in this world by taking two steps to the right instead of two to the left? By crossing the street and walking on the other side? All the difference in the world. The scariest thing about life to me is how many options there are and that you are surrounded by them all the time. We have only to act.

On 11 May 2007, at 12:02, karin@lotsalegs.com wrote:

rob, I can't even speak right now, Im so upset. I cried all night. you are so amazing, you have given me so much and I thank you for everything.

when I think, if we hadn't met in that parking lot…

On 11 May 2007, at 10:17, rob baltusrol wrote:

Karin;

Now you know why I hate the phone.

From: Andy Read
To: Rob Baltusrol
Subj:

O'Reilly just called for hearings!

So much for the coffee and kitchen table, my friend. Onto the rope!

To: Andy Read
From: Rob Baltusrol
Subj: re:

It's smart. He's going for the ratings, he wants to be first. (Clemenza was always smarter.)

On 11 May 2007, at 15:52, andy read wrote:

O'Reilly just called for hearings!

So much for the coffee and kitchen table, my friend. Onto the rope!

To: Andy Read
From: Rob Baltusrol
Subj: re:

In places like Bangladesh, when a storm's coming, they don't shut the doors they open them. Let it blow through. That's what's happening here. They want this over as fast as possible.

They're all fucking lawyers, they're thinking double jeopardy. What they're forgetting: guilty as charged.

On 11 May 2007, at 15:52, andy read wrote:

O'Reilly just called for hearings!

So much for the coffee and kitchen table, my friend. Onto the rope!

To: Charles Wilcon
From: Rob Baltusrol
Subj: re:

Malvern returns!!

On 12 May 2007, at 9:29, charles wilcon wrote:

Bloody hell?!? When did all this start?

From: Andy Read
To: Rob Baltusrol
Subj: re: ady for my closeup

Tessio!!

HA!

On 11 May 2007, at 16:02, rob baltusrol wrote:

It's smart. He's going for the ratings, he wants to be first. (Clemenza was always smarter.)

On 11 May 2007, at 15:52, andy read wrote:

O'Reilly just called for hearings!

So much for the coffee and kitchen table, my friend. Onto the rope!

From: karin@lotsalegs.com
To: Rob Baltusrol
Subj: re:

eat it!!

On 11 May 2007, at 18:31, rob baltusrol wrote:

What am I going to do with this zucchini?

To: Andy Read
From: Rob Baltusrol
Subj:

Griffith just called. He and Jones are driving up. We're gonna share cross-examination but both felt I should be the face of this thing, do most of the questioning, and asked if I'd mind. (Talk about liking cookies!)

I tell you, bro, there is nothing Perry Mason about this. More like Florence Henderson finding out which of the kids ate the chocolate icing. Good bet it's the one with the icing all over his face. (Cindy?)

Why were you flying so slow? Who ordered it? What was his name?
Next!

Did you see any bodies in the field? Any luggage? Any PLANE? No?
What was there?
Some smoke.
Some smoke?
And a hole in the ground.
A hole in the ground. How big was the hole in the ground?
Not big.
How big?
About the size of a car, maybe. A little smaller.
Smaller than a car?
Yeah. I'd say.
And did it occur to you that maybe this wasn't the scene of a plane crash?
A big commercial plane?
Yeah, well, that's what I said.
You did? To who?
The police, investigators. Anyone who'd listen.

That's the way it's going to go, And. Trust me. The butler did it.

Draft Folder
subj: journal

All the bullshit, all the fuckups, all the failures; all the assholes, all the asswipe jobs; the shitty cars, the clueless, gutless hack bosses, the backstabbers, the disrespect; the women whose emails stopped coming, the friends who left, the lonely pathetic solitary existence.

That all ends tonight.

Just be yourself.

Within reason.

Xxx

This is like Karate Kid. All those brush strokes are starting to make sense.

Xxxx

Warm, positive, powerful … who needs drinking?

From: karin@lotsalegs.com
To: Rob Baltusrol
Subj: re: I Just Saw A Face

rob, there's something else, I hope you don't mind… it's that tape
we made. can I have it? do you mind? I know you have a lot more
to lose than me, and you wouldn't do anything with it, I know that.
but still.. it's me on there, mostly, doing those things. (If my dad
saw!) I guess I just want it, thats all.. do you mind?

On 11 May 2007, at 5:33, rob baltusrol wrote:

Had it been another day, I might have looked the other way…

To: karin@lotsalegs
From: Rob Baltusrol
Subj: re:

Understand completely. I'll send it out today or tomorrow.

(You do not know how it pains me to have to part with that.) (Couldn't we have joint custody?)

On 12 May 2007, at 20:35, karin@lotsalegs.com wrote:

rob, there's something else, I hope you don't mind... it's that tape we made. can I have it? do you mind? I know you have a lot more to lose than me, and you wouldn't do anything with it, I know that. but still.. it's me on there, mostly, doing those things. (If my dad saw!) I guess I just want it, thats all.. do you mind?

On 11 May 2007, at 5:33, rob baltusrol wrote:

Had it been another day, I might have looked the other way...

To: Andy Read
From: Rob Baltusrol
Subj: re:

What were the lies you were referring to?

On 13 May 2007, at 10:02, andy read wrote:

Here come the lies, my friend, just like you said. According to Newsweek, from their website, you have a chronic inability to hold a job, a son born on Medicaid, were rarely seen sober at BU, owes thousands in child support, have collected unemployment at least half a dozen times, owes every utility company in Ulster County, and, my favorite, has, according to someone in our hometown, "crashed just about every car he's driven." (Wasn't me!)

To: Andy Read
From: Rob Baltusrol
Subj: re:

Speaking of sober: before I finally decided to quit drinking, during those ten years I was planning when I would, a lot of games were played: how bad was I last night? Did anyone know I was drunk? Did I pull it off? How about work? (How bad was I last Wednesday?) Then, after one drunk too many, I finally decided it was really time to quit and I knew this time it was serious because I could honestly say: I'd rather the whole world thought I was drinking, and I wasn't, than thought I wasn't, and I was.

And from that simple truth I have gained all my strength. To the point where it no longer applies to just drinking, it applies to everything.

On 13 May 2007, at 10:02, andy read wrote:

Here come the lies, my friend, just like you said. According to Newsweek, from their website, you have a chronic inability to hold a job, a son born on Medicaid, were rarely seen sober at BU, owes thousands in child support, have collected unemployment at least half a dozen times, owes every utility company in Ulster County, and, my favorite, has, according to someone in our hometown, "crashed just about every car he's driven." (Wasn't me!)

To: Sebastian Baltusrol
From: Rob Baltusrol
Subj: Grasshopper

Sebastian;

"When you can grab the pebble from my hand..."

It must seem to you sometimes that I still think you're eight years old, and I'm packing you for an overnight— the toothpaste, the toothbrush, the sweater, the soap — but the fact is you are much older now and know all those things you can do without for one night. And it's time I stopped packing.

Parents, Sebastian, we mean well, we really do, but sometimes we say things we don't mean. And it's not dishonesty, it's simply trying to look out for the most important things in the world to us, our children.

And all parents tell their children not to play near the train tracks, Sebastian. But it's a lie. It's exactly where we want you to play. We want you to get as close to the train as possible. We just don't want to see you to get killed.

(Look! The pebble! It's gone!!!)

Now brush your teeth and go to bed.

167

To: Andy Read
From: Rob Baltusrol
Subj: re:

Of course they were dazed! They didn't know which expression to use!

On 11 May 2007, at 13:02, andy read wrote:

Rob;

Just went into town: it is all anyone's talking about. At the top of that hill in Ipswich -- remember the roundabout -- looking down. No one was walking! All you could see were groups of people STANDING, then other people joining them. (I thought of Mr. Martin's class and those beads of water.)

At the hardware store. Two groups of people, inside and out. Just talking. (Worse day for commerce in town's history.)

The book store: there was a line. Not checking out, the phone! Mal was letting everyone call Washington or Boston, the numbers he'd written on a blackboard.

Went into the diner, absolutely quiet except for the TVs. You could not hear a glass, a fork. The cash register made some noise, and the owner looked over and stared at her employee -- for ringing up a sale!

On CNN, shots of senate offices and staff members running around, in and out of offices, carrying papers, some were laughing. A groups of grim-faced senators or congressmen. The switchboards are being jammed, my friend. JAMMED! And the anchors on CNN, they were lost. They were dazed. They were absolutely dazed!!

From: Joanna Wallen
To: Rob Baltusrol
Subj: re: Family Docs

Rob: Frumpa says he'd love to do it!! (He flew with Pan Am!!!)
Tell us what's next!!
Joanna.

On 28 April 2007, at 19:32, rob baltusrol wrote:

Joanna;

It was nice meeting you the other day, seeing your shop and meeting your great-grandfather, hearing some of his tales. And it has belatedly occurred to me: I run a side business: shooting family documentaries, documentaries of everyday families. You may have seen my ad: You Are the Story. (Subhead: Families … it's where the action is.)

Included with the documentary is a questionnaire, some sample questions are below. I thought your grandfather might enjoy taking a look. Cheers.

Rob Baltusrol

1. What is your all-time favorite residence? (Address.)

2. What album has provided you with the most hours of listening pleasure?

3. What do you believe is the truest thing ever said?

4. Are you more or less comforted by a conspicuous police presence?

5. Have you ever shoplifted?

6. What's the most valuable course you ever took, college or high school?

7. Have you ever flown Pan Am?

8. About what action taken in your life do you most wish someone had urged you to reconsider?

9. Which color property do you prefer owning in Monopoly?

10. Have you ever seen a ghost?

To: Andy Read
From: Rob Baltusrol
Subj: re:

And I was right! I was right! We are the story after all. We're the blonde girl gone missing in Aruba!

On 11 May 2007, at 13:02, andy read wrote:

Rob;

Just went into town: it is all anyone's talking about. At the top of that hill in Ipswich -- remember the roundabout -- looking down. No one was walking! All you could see were groups of people STANDING, then other people joining them. (I thought of Mr. Martin's class and those beads of water.)

At the hardware store. Two groups of people, inside and out. Just talking. (Worse day for commerce in town's history.)

The book store: there was a line. Not checking out, the phone! Mal was letting everyone call Washington or Boston, the numbers he'd written on a blackboard.

Went into the diner, absolutely quiet except for the TVs. You could not hear a glass, a fork. The cash register made some noise, and the owner looked over and stared at her employee -- for ringing up a sale!

On CNN, shots of senate offices and staff members running around, in and out of offices, carrying papers, some were laughing. A groups of grim-faced senators or congressmen. The switchboards are being jammed, my friend. JAMMED! And the anchors on CNN, they were lost. They were dazed. They were absolutely dazed!!

From: British-American Educational Foundation
To: Rob Baltusrol
Subj: hearings

rob;

board feels it's probably best you not mention BAEF
affiliation. for what it's worth, I strongly disagreed. (I think
Madeleine would be proud.)
wil

From: Andy Read
To: Rob Baltusrol
Subj:

Rob:

I wanted to write you something important before the big day, just to let
you know how much you've meant to me over the years, what our
friendship has meant and I've started this email so many times and finally
Cind said, Andy: when you think of Rob, what's the first thing you think
of?

And she was right: and this is what I think of. You mentioned sixth grade,
I remember fourth, and Miss Buckout's class. We were having a party, it
was someone's birthday, it was the end of the day and there was cake and
we were listening to records and you had brought in a Beatles album
(Revolver?) someone else had brought in Herman's Hermits so the class
took a vote which to listen to. And the class overwhelmingly, it was
unanimous (me too!) voted for Herman's Hermits. And you stood up --- I
will never forget this -- and you said, "What, are you people nuts?!? No
one's going to remember Herman's Hermit's, the Beatles will last
forever!!!" It was 40 years ago, but I remember it as if it was yesterday
and still have never seen anyone more certain of anything in my life. And
of course you were right.

That's the person we need you to be tomorrow, my friend. Be that person
and it's how we'll all remember you.

Beatles Forever!

Andy

To: Andy Read
From: Rob Baltusrol
Subj: re:

Rubber Soul. And "Mrs. Brown You've Got a Lovely Daughter" is the
perfect pop tune.

You'll never know how much those words mean to me, And, how much I
needed to hear them.

Now: let's rock and roll.

Love ya pal

Rob

On 14 May 2007, at 20:09, andy read wrote:

Rob:

I wanted to write you something important before the big day, just to let
you know how much you've meant to me over the years, what our
friendship has meant and I've started this email so many times and finally
Cind said, Andy: when you think of Rob, what's the first thing you think
of?

And she was right: and this is what I think of. You mentioned sixth grade,
I remember fourth, and Miss Buckout's class. We were having a party, it
was someone's birthday, it was the end of the day and there was cake and
we were listening to records and you had brought in a Beatles album
(Revolver?) someone else had brought in Herman's Hermits so the class
took a vote which to listen to. And the class overwhelmingly, it was
unanimous (me too!) voted for Herman's Hermits. And you stood up --- I
will never forget this -- and you said, "What, are you people nuts?!? No
one's going to remember Herman's Hermit's, the Beatles will last
forever!!!" It was 40 years ago, but I remember it as if it was yesterday
and still have never seen anyone more certain of anything in my life. And
of course you were right.

That's the person we need you to be tomorrow, my friend. Be that person
and it's how we'll all remember you.

Beatles Forever!

Andy

To: British-American Educational Foundation
From: Rob Baltusrol
Subj: re: hearings

Thanks, Wil.

I thought of Madeleine the other day. I remember how after our interview, after she had decided I should go to Malvern and was walking me to the front door she suddenly said, "Oh, and if you had ever wanted to be someone else, now would be the time."

I couldn't believe it. (How she must have wished I'd taken her advice!)

Rob

On 14 May 2007, at 19:29, wil jeffries at baef.org wrote:

rob;

board feels it's probably best you not mention BAEF affiliation. for what it's worth, I strongly disagreed. (I think Madeleine would be proud.)

wil

To: karin@lotsalegs.com
From: Rob Baltusrol
Subj: re:

I'll tell him.

(And don't forget. I get it for holidays.)

Wish me luck, babe.

On 14 May 2007, at 20:32, karin@lotsalegs.com wrote:

I got the tape today, rob, just like I knew I would, I knew I would...
so how exactly do I tell my father that the jews greatest enemy
happens to be the finest person this jew has ever known.. any
advice there, smart guy?

From: British-American Educational Foundation
To: Rob Baltusrol
Subj: re: hearings

not now she wouldn't rob.

On 14 May 2007, at 20:02, rob baltusrol wrote:

Thanks, Wil.

I thought of Madeleine the other day. I remember how after our interview, after she had decided I should go to Malvern and was walking me to the front door she suddenly said, "Oh, and if you had ever wanted to be someone else, now would be the time."

I couldn't believe it. (How she must have wished I'd taken her advice!)

Rob

On 14 May 2007, at 19:29, wil jeffries at baef.org wrote:

rob;
board feels it's probably best you not mention BAEF affiliation. for what it's worth, I strongly disagreed. (I think Madeleine would be proud.)
wil

To: Andy Read
From: Rob Baltusrol
Subj: re:

Yeah, there was some discussion here on that too, but: the English may think the whole monarchy thing is bullshit, but just try finding one who won't drop to his knees upon seeing the Queen. Same with the Times. People may hate it, not trust it, but somehow (still!) they believe it. And when I asked him why he used the word "push" and he wriggled and said, "Uh... well, actually, that wasn't my word," everyone listening sat up. Then and there everyone knew the fix was on, it was US vs. THEM.

On 15 May 2007, at 16:13, andy read wrote:

Very interesting, calling the Times reporter first. Very shrewd.

(Liked the blue jeans too.)

To: Andy Read
From: Rob Baltusrol
Subj: re:

Yeah, did the whole Woodstock thing. Keep 'em guessing. (Those were my clean jeans, by the way.)

Tomorrow: the suit! (My funeral?!?) I might even shave.

On 15 May 2007, at 16:13, andy read wrote:

Interesting choice, calling the Times reporter first. Very, very shrewd.

(Liked the blue jeans too.)

To: Andy Read
From: Rob Baltusrol
Subj: re:

Yeah. Me, too.

On 15 May 2007, at 21:55, andy read wrote:

Kind of lost me there, Obi Wan, but go for it.

On 15 May 2007, at 21:17, rob baltusrol wrote:

People are going to see what they see and hear what they hear but they
still need to read about it. To make sure it happened. They still need to see
the headline. Just like reading about a ballgame they attended.

If I can make the message, then I can tell them what the press is going to
say the next day and the press is trapped; like a blackjack dealer having to
go on 16. Only I'm the dealer.

When predicting history is making history, you're pretty much
unstoppable. So if I can combine making history with predicting history,
well they're the same thing. Point at the sky when lightning strikes, they'll
be calling you Merlin.

To: Helen Wicker
From: Rob Baltusrol
Subj:

Mom, sorry about the phone call, I understand why you're upset. I do.
(Amazing, isn't it, how after all these years, both of us with only good
intentions, that all we ever seem to do is misunderstand each other?)

Nobody's going to kill me, Mom. Trust me. I've never seen things so
clearly in my life. I am going to win. They don't stand a chance. I am
going to win then I'll disappear and no one will ever hear from me again.

I know some things too.

To: Charles Wilcon
From: Rob Baltusrol
Subj: re:

Only question: does Bindy have a TV?

On 12 May 2007, at 9:29, charles wilcon wrote:

Bloody hell?!? When did all this start?

To: Helen Wicker
From: Rob Baltusrol
Subj:

And by the way, Mom: Claire was kind enough to point out that it's been you who's been keeping me in wheels all these years, so again, much thanks. (About that Datsun…)

From: Public/NYT/NYTIMES
To: Rob Baltusrol
Subj: re: well they did float

Thank you for contacting the Public Editor. An associate or I read every message. Because of the volume of e-mail, we cannot respond personally to every message, but we forward many messages to appropriate newsroom staffers and follow up to be sure concerns raised in those messages are treated with serious consideration. If a further reply is warranted, you will be hearing from us shortly.

Requests for corrections should be submitted to nytnews@nytimes.com. If you are dissatisfied with the response, please let us know.

When referring to a specific article, please include its date, section and headline.

To: public@nytimes
From: Rob Basltusrol
Subj: well they did float

Editor;

The Queen Mary and SS France? Cruise ships?? They were ocean liners!

And the QE2? Last of the great liners? It was a cruise ship.

And they were crossings, not voyages.

Do you guys get anything right?

Rob Baltusrol

From: Claire Tansil
To: Rob Baltusrol
Subj: Apology

Rob;

This emails a long time coming, not just days, but years, and for that I'm truly sorry.

There's obviously a lot more to you than I ever gave you credit for, things you were right about that I was wrong about, and I hope you will accept this very sincere if belated apology.

I love you very much, I always have, and have always been proud of you, yes, even if I've never shown that at all. You have always been your own person and that's been hard for me to accept at times. Only now do I understand why. (I'm putting you in front of the fireplace.)

Dick Cheney's an asshole. Go get him!

Claire.

To: Claire Tansil
From: Rob Baltusrol
Subj: That old devil moon

Claire;

Thank you very much for that.

I think you and I have done each other a great disservice through the years
by always presuming to know all there is to know about the other. I'm
sure we are both wrong. You, for instance, I am sure don't know that
(thanks to Buckley) Finian's Rainbow has always remained my favorite
musical. (A lie: after My Fair Lady.)

You ain't seen nothing yet.

Love,

Rob

On 16 May 2007, at 20:31, claire tansil wrote:

Rob;

This emails a long time coming, not just days, but years, and for that I'm
truly sorry.

There's obviously a lot more to you than I ever gave you credit for, things
you were right about that I was wrong about, and I hope you will accept
this very sincere if belated apology.

I love you very much, I always have, and have always been proud of you,
yes, even if I've never shown that at all. You have always been your own
person and that's been hard for me to accept at times. Only now do I
understand why. (I'm putting you in front of the fireplace.)

Dick Cheney's an asshole. Go get him!

Claire.

To: Andy Read
From: Rob Baltusrol
Subj:

Sebastian;

In that play I wrote — the one I lost when I lost my hard drive — you
remember your father, staring out at the floor at Best Buy for 30 minutes
after the tech guy told him he'd never seen a hard drive wiped so clean —
that play. But one line I do remember from it is when the lead character
says, "Sara, I really do believe everyone has just one decision in their life
they've got to get right."

I don't know if it's relevant or not to your situation, but it's one of the only
lines I remember from the play — such a play! — so maybe I remember it
for a reason.

From: Andy Read
To: Rob Baltusrol
Subj:

Bro:

Almost a riot at Best Buy. People were gathered around the TVs watching, hundreds, crowd got so big and management tried to bust it up, nobody moved. Cops were called in, still no one moved until after your press briefing.. (No one bought anything, either.)

Then on 95 south there was a huge traffic jam, people flooding to DC, answering your call, and troopers had set up a road block and then someone got into their car and the troopers pulled their gun and the cars kept going… all of them. Trooper didn't fire.

To: Andy Read
From: Rob Baltusrol
Subj: re:

We're running full speed now, bro, just hoping someone will open the doors before we smash against them, bust our noses.

Reminds me of being chased once by some kids when I was real young, six or so, it wasn't my neighborhood, and every back yard I ran into there was a hole in the fence that allowed me to escape. That's what this is like. I don't think I got away so much as they just gave up.

Of course lost in that story is why I was running in the first place.

(You don't think his gun jammed, do you?)

On 16 May 2007, at 18:40, andy read wrote:

Bro:

Almost a riot at Best Buy. People were gathered around the TVs watching, hundreds, crowd got so big and management tried to bust it up, nobody moved. Cops were called in, still no one moved until after your press briefing.. (No one bought anything, either.)

Then on 95 south there was a huge traffic jam, people flooding to DC, answering your call, and troopers had set up a road block and then someone got into their car and the troopers pulled their gun and the cars kept going… all of them. Trooper didn't fire.

To: Sebastian Baltusrol
From: Rob Baltusrol
Subj: re:

I was afraid you'd ask that.

He made the wrong one, Sebastian. He let her go.

On 16 May 2007, at 21:22, sebastion baltusrol wrote:

What decision did that character make? Do you remember?

On 16 May 2007, at 21:02, rob baltusrol wrote:

Sebastian;

In that play I wrote — the one I lost when I lost my hard drive — you remember your father, staring out at the floor at Best Buy for 30 minutes after the tech guy told him he'd never seen a hard drive wiped so clean — that play. But one line I do remember from it is when the lead character says, "Sara, I really do believe everyone has just one decision in their life they've got to get right."

I don't know if it's relevant or not to your situation, but it's one of the only lines I remember from the play — such a play! — so maybe I remember it for a reason.

To: Andy Read
From: Rob Baltusrol
Subj: re:

zzzzz....

On 16 May 2007, at 22:14, andy read wrote:

Not to put any pressure on you or anything, but I just read where some 5 billion people will be watching you go against Cheney tomorrow.

Sleep well, my friend.

To: Sebastian Baltusrol
From: Rob Baltusrol
Subj: what else

I love you, Sebastian.

From: Andy Read
To: Rob Baltusrol
Subj:

Was that the longest five minutes in recorded history or what?!?!

How did you know Cheney wouldn't answer? How did you wait??? What tipped you off??

When you said, "Did you at least knock them out first or did you just crash the planes," and Cheney made that weird look--even for him--and looked up at the ceiling then out the window then you waited and waited and waited and finally he said, "We just crashed the planes…" !!! Unfuckinbelievable.

And what about the stenographer?

I'm dazed. Just dazed. Awestruck and dazed. Unfuckinbelievable.

To: Andy Read
From: Rob Baltusrol
Subj: re:

The stenographer was pure theatre. (Think Bill Clinton, biting his lower lip.) I knew exactly where that testimony was located. So when I asked him to read back from Tuesday morning, somewhere around 10:37, when Minetta was talking about the planes and he picked up on the sentence virtually from where I had left off… And the room gasped …

It was beautiful. I almost started laughing. Really. Cheney knew it too, he stared at me but there was nothing he could say.

On 17 May 2007, at 16:02, andy read wrote:

Was that the longest five minutes in recorded history or what?!?!

How did you know Cheney wouldn't answer? How did you wait??? What tipped you off??

When you said, "Did you at least knock them out first or did you just crash the planes," and Cheney made that weird look--even for him--and looked up at the ceiling then out the window then you waited and waited and waited and finally he said, "We just crashed the planes…" Unfuckinbelievable.

And what about the stenographer?

I'm dazed. Just dazed. Awestruck and dazed. Unfuckinbelievable.

From: Andy Read
To: Rob Baltusrol
Subj: re:

What tipped you off?

On 17 May 2007, at 16:44, rob baltusrol wrote:

The stenographer was pure theatre. (Think Bill Clinton, biting his lower lip.) I knew exactly where that testimony was located. So when I asked him to read back from Tuesday morning, somewhere around 10:37, when Minetta was talking about the planes and he picked up on the sentence virtually from where I had left off… And the room gasped …

It was beautiful. I almost started laughing. Really. Cheney knew it too, he stared at me but there was nothing he could say.

On 17 May 2007, at 16:02, andy read wrote:

Was that the longest five minutes in recorded history or what?!?!

How did you know Cheney wouldn't answer? How did you wait??? What tipped you off??

When you said, "Did you at least knock them out first or did you just crash the planes," and Cheney made that weird look--even for him--and looked up at the ceiling then out the window then you waited and waited and waited and finally he said, "We just crashed the planes…" Unfuckinbelievable.

And what about the stenographer?

I'm dazed. Just dazed. Awestruck and dazed. Unfuckinbelievable.

To: Andy Read
From: Rob Baltusrol
Subj: re:

Ah…

You're not going to believe this. I wrote a script called Bad Rice. (Still can't believe I didn't sell that thing.) And in the script the lead character's name is Renay. But if you haven't seen it spelled you'd assume it was spelled Rene. And when Cheney said that about the Pennsylvania plane -- "had" I think he said, not "if" -- it reminded me of the script, that Cheney must have known beforehand.

And that's when I realized what Cheney had done. And when I stood up, and looked out the window, and saw all those people on the lawn, I just lost it. I started sobbing and couldn't stop. I was so stressed and I either could fight it or let it go and because I still wasn't done I decided to let it go, and when I poured that pitcher of water over my head --that wasn't stage managed at all. It absolutely was what I needed to do.

And then Cheney made his fatal mistake: he asked to use the bathroom. (For what? We'll never know.) And that's when I got the marine involved, and getting the marine involved was key. Up until that point it was me against Cheney, after I got the marine involved it was Cheney against us. Cheney then said it could wait but by that point it was too late, by the time the marine went back to where he was standing he was officially on OUR SIDE! (An image! Again! The best! In uniform!)

Absolutely key. A huge risk, but we needed the marine. The third hole in the fence.

Then I told Cheney I'm gonna ask you three questions and you're not going to answer any of them, and then I asked that first question (please, Lord, oh please) and he didn't answer, just looked down at the table …

It was over.

On 17 May 2007, at 16:48, andy read wrote:

What tipped you off?

On 17 May 2007, at 16:44, rob baltusrol wrote:

Draft Folder
subj: journal

All the bullshit, all the fuckups, all the failures; all the assholes, all the asswipe jobs; the shitty cars, the clueless, gutless hack bosses, the backstabbers, the disrespect; the women whose emails stopped coming, the friends who left, the lonely pathetic solitary existence.

That all ends tonight.

Just be yourself.

Within reason.

Xxx

This is like Karate Kid. All those brush strokes are starting to make sense.

Xxxx

Warm, positive, powerful … who needs drinking?

Xxx

Remember at some point to compare the media to a rodeo clown. In daily press conferences?

Predict Times's quote of the day -- (win if they do, win if they don't.)

Xxxx

!

From: Andy Read
To: Rob Baltusrol
Subj:

Un fucking believable.

Across the towers. And the crowd is cheering.

From: Sebastian Baltusrol
To: Rob Baltusrol
Subj:

Dad;
When you started crying and poured the pitcher of water over your head, I swear I thought it was over but Mom grabbed by arm and said, "no wait."

And I looked at her and she was staring right at the TV and she said, "He's fine."

From: karin@lotsalegs.com
To: Rob Baltusrol
Subj: YAHOO!!!!

Rob;

I'll never forget our first night together, when we all did was talk and
you know what. And you told me that it is accepted that when you
go down a hill on a sled you're going to hit a tree, but that the crash
is part of the ride. And that's true everywhere, you said. And
watching you on tv, you taking those bastards on, with the troops
coming in through the doors, you looking them in the eye, I kept
thinking, he's going to crash, he's going to crash, but you never did!
And then when the guard came over asked Cheney to stand our
entire building was cheering, we were crying, Rob we all were.

Rob: my father too.

To: Sebastian Baltusrol
From: Rob Baltusrol
Subj: re:

She has her moments, Sebastian.

On 17 May 2007, at 16:11, sebastian baltusrol wrote:

Dad;
When you started crying and poured the pitcher of water over your head, I swear I thought it was over but Mom grabbed by arm and said, "no wait."

And I looked at her and she was staring right at the TV and she said, "He's fine."

From: karin@lotsalegs.com
To: Rob Baltusrol
Subj:

And let everyone else think of you as the guy that took down a government. I'll always remember you as the guy in the parking lot who turned to me after his car made some godawful noise and said, "she's a beauty, isn't she?"

It's when I fell in love.

From: Andy Read
To: Rob Baltusrol
Subj:

Well they finally did something right. The Times gave you their quotation of the day: "My country doesn't need me, your country needs you!"

I'm gonna miss you, pal. Have a good time in Amsterdam, or wherever you end up.

You did it, you mad fucker. You fucking did it. (And you were right--it was easy!)

Love,

Andy

To: Andy Read
From: Rob Baltusrol
Subj: ...Gee our old La Salle ran great

And;

We'll always have email.

(And personally, I would have gone with: "If my country needs me, then my country is in a lot worse shape than even I ever imagined.")

Thanks for everything, it absolutely could not have been done without you. (You, Matt Cantor, the cop, and the marine.) (pssss.. and bill o'reilly...) (And James Shen.)

Oh, and say, listen: I've got this idea ...

On 18 May 2007, at 10:09, andy read wrote:

Well they finally did something right. The Times gave you their quotation of the day: "My country doesn't need me, your country needs you!"

I'm gonna miss you, pal. Have a good time in Amsterdam, or wherever you end up.

You did it, you mad fucker. You did it. (You were right--it was easy!)

Love,

Andy

From: karin@lotsalegs.com
To: Rob Baltusrol
Subj: re:

congratulations, Rob. i'm happy for you. it's where you belong.
(I hope she's ready for you!!)

karin

On 24 May 2007, at 15:55, rob baltusrol wrote:

Just so you know, sweetie, I'll be heading overseas, …

Anything you ever need, anytime, pick up the phone, er, email.

One for the ages, doll. One for the ages.

Rob

From: Marcello Robertson
To: Rob Baltusrol
Subj: re: Bad Rice

I'll pass.

On 10 May 2007, at 16:44, rob baltusrol wrote:

Dear Marcello;

Thank you for your email, though obviously I would have liked its
contents to be different.

I have another script, if you're interested. It's about an alcoholic whose
decision to quit drinking turns out to be the worst decision of his life. And
believe it or not, it's a comedy too.

I can send it if you like. Cheers.

Rob.

On 9 May 2007, at 10:40, marcello robertson
<robertsonentertainment.com> wrote:

Thank you for letting me read Bad Rice, but I
must say I didn't find the script to be funny at
all. In fact, I'm not sure I laughed once. But I
thank you for letting me read it and wish you all
the best.
Marcello

To: Sebastian Baltusrol
From: Rob Baltusrol
Subj: onwards and upwards!

Sebastian;

Believe it or not, your old man just might be able to parlay this little stint
into some honest-to-goodness employment. Better yet: several universities
in Europe, Paris and Amsterdam among them, have expressed an interest
in my teaching a journalism/writing course (that's what they think!) so
looks like you're stuck with me a little while longer. (Separate journeys,
common ports.)

You'll have many wonderful experiences in your life, Sebastian, but this
has been the first great one. And know you stood tall. Know too that I
couldn't have done it without you and I apologize for putting you in a
situation, so early, where I depended so much on you and not you on me.

I know you think I reminisce a lot, Sebastian (not another Malvern story!),
it's not really true. I do go back on occasion, however. I revisit. And rarely
do you revisit where you were or what you did, I find, you revisit how you
felt. Maybe, even, sadly, to appreciate those feelings for the first time. But
you're smarter than me, you always have been, dear son, and are
appreciating those feelings already.

Never go against your heart, Sebastian. Never. It's the only thing in this
world you can trust. (And me, of course.)

LOVE

DAD

ABOUT THE AUTHOR

Nick Baam lives in Paris. Malvern was written in Charleston.

malvernthenovel.com

48381231R00125

Made in the USA
Middletown, DE
16 June 2019